Spring
=Harvest

SPRING HARVEST PRAISE 1996

Music Edition

Published by Spring Harvest 14 Horsted Square, Uckfield, East Sussex TN22 1QL. Spring Harvest. A Registered Charity.

Cover design by Clark and Clark.
Illustrations by Ben Ecclestone.
Layout and additional illustrations by Ron Bryant-Funnell.
Printed by Redwood Books, Trowbridge, Wiltshire.

Spring Harvest wishes to acknowledge and thank the following people for their help in the compilation and production of this songbook:
Dave Pope, Jonny Baker, Charlie Groves, Robert Lamont, David Langford, Simon Moodie, Andy Piercy, Chris Redgate, Noel Richards, Isobel Waspe, Laura Werts and Head Office Staff.

ISBN 1-899788-11-5

Distributed to the UK Christian trade by ICC, Silverdale Road, Eastbourne, Eastbourne, East Sussex BN20 7AB.

Introduction

WELCOME to the 1996 Spring Harvest Songbook. This compilation has been put together carefully and prayerfully. It is designed to reflect the broad spectrum of worship material that is used at the Spring Harvest event, but can be easily transferred into a local church situation.

Our aim is that this songbook should enable all of us to concentrate on our God during worship. To meet with him – rather than simply sing about him. There are familiar hymns and songs which proclaim the truths of the Christian faith with clarity and confidence. Their very familiarity allows us to concentrate afresh on those truths.

In contrast there are many new songs – from around the world - which bring fresh vibrancy to our worship. Songs ancient and modern, meditative and demonstrative, high praise and intimate worship, all are to be found in these pages. Our God is a God of creativity and variety. As we worship him at Spring Harvest and in our local churches we want our worship to reflect those same characteristics.

It has always been one of our very highest priorities at Spring Harvest to try to resource and serve the local church. It is my prayer and intention that this edition will strengthen that resolve. May these songs be an encouragement and blessing to all who use them – but primarily may they help us give heart expression of our worship to the God who deserves the very best.

Dave Pope

1   Above The Clash Of Creeds
(No Other Way)

♩ = 120

Graham Kendrick

1. A - bove___ the clash___ of creeds,___ the ma - ny
2. Be - fore___ we called___ he came___ to earth___ from
3. Be - neath___ the cross___ of Christ___ let earth___ fall

voi - ces that call___ on so ma - ny names,___
hea - ven, our ma - ker be - came___ a man;___
si - lent in awe___ of this my - ster - y,___

in - to___ these fi - nal days___
when no - one else___ could pay___
then let___ this song___ a - rise___

our God___ has spo - ken by send - ing
he bought___ our free - dom, ex - chan - ging
and fill___ the na - tions: O hear___ him

2   All Hail The Power

Words after Edward Perronet and John Rippon
in this version Jubilate Hymns
Music: William Shrubsole, Arr. Roger Mayor

With strength ♩ = 128

1. All hail the power of Je - sus'___name! let
(2) crown him, moon and stars of___night; he
(3) him, you mar - tyrs spurn - ing___pain, who
(4) all who trust in Christ ex - claim in
(5) in that fi - nal judge - ment__ hour when

kings be - fore him fall,   his power and ma - jes -
made you,___great and small: bright sun, praise him who
wit - nessed___ to his call;   now sing your vic - tory -
won - der,___ to re - call   the one who bore our
all re - bel - lions fall,   we'll rise in his tri -

3

All I Once Held Dear
(Knowing You)

Phil 3: 7-11
Graham Kendrick

♩ = 65

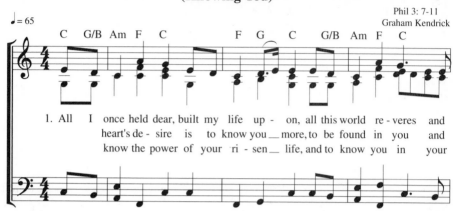

1. All I once held dear, built my life up - on, all this world re - veres and
heart's de - sire is to know you __ more, to be found in you and
know the power of your ri - sen __ life, and to know you in your

wars to own; all I once thought gain I have coun - ted __ loss - spent and
known as yours; to pos - sess by faith what I could not __ earn - all - sur-
suf - fer - ings; to be - come like you in your death, my __ Lord, so with

worth - less now, com - pared to this.
pass - ing gift of right - eous - ness. Know - ing you, Je - sus,
you to live and ne - ver die!

know-ing you, there is no great-er thing: you're my

all, you're the best, you're my joy, my right-eous-ness; and I love you, Lord.

To end

2. Now my
3. Oh to love you, Lord, love you, Lord.

4 All That I Am

With feeling ♩ = 76

James Wright

All that I am, I lay be-fore you; all I pos-sess, Lord, I con-fess, is no-thing with-out you. Sa-viour and King, I now en-throne you: take my life, my liv-ing sa-cri-fice to you.

5 Almighty God

Words: from The Alternative
Service Book 1980
Music: A. Piercy, D. Clifton
& C. Groves

Al-might-y God, to whom all hearts be o - pen,

all des-ires known, and from whom no sec-rets are hid - den:

cleanse the thoughts of our hearts by the

in - spi - ra - tion of your Ho - ly Spi - rit,

that we may per-fect-ly love you, and worth-i-ly mag-ni-fy;

that we may per-fect-ly love you and worth-i-ly mag-ni-fy your

ho - ly name; through Christ our Lord. A - men;

through Christ our Lord. A - men.

And Can It Be

6

Words: Charles Wesley
Music: Thomas Campbell's Bouquet
Arr. Chris Norton

1. And can it be that I should gain an interest in the Saviour's blood? Died he for me, who caused his pain; for me, who him to
2. 'Tis mystery all! - the Immortal dies,- who can explore his strange design? In vain the first-born seraph tries to sound the depths of
3. He left his Father's throne above- so free, so infinite his grace- emptied himself of all but love, and bled for Adam's
4. Long my imprisoned spirit lay fast bound in sin and nature's night: thine eye diffused a quickening ray; I woke- the dungeon

5. No condemnation now I dread;
   Jesus, and all in him, is mine!
   Alive in him, my living head,
   and clothed in righteousness divine,
   bold I approach the eternal throne
   and claim the crown through Christ my own.

7 And His Love Goes On
(Look What God Has Done)

Graham Kendrick

And his love goes on and on for - ev - er.

1. Look what God has done for us ov - er all the years we've shared, ev - er since the day al - so
2. Look at all we've shared in him; joy and laugh -ter, tears and pain, grace to car - ry on when
3. Free - ly we have all re - ceived, free -ly we must give, think -ing of _ the price he

Profession of faith

Lord, you have always given
Bread for the coming day,
And though I am poor,
Today I believe

Lord, you have always given
Strength for the coming day,
And though I am weak,
Today I believe

Lord, you have always given
Peace for the coming day,
And though of anxious heart,
Today I believe

Lord, you have always kept
Me safe in trials,
And now, tried as I am,
Today I believe

Lord, you have always marked
The road for the coming day,
And though it may be hidden,
Today I believe

Lord, you have always lightened
This darkness of mine,
And though the night is here,
Today I believe

Lord, you have always spoken
When the time was ripe,
And though you be silent now,
Today I believe.

8

Be Still, For The Presence Of The Lord

David Evans
Arr. Geoff Baker

Flowing ♩ = 85

1. Be still, for the pre-sence of the Lord, the ho - ly One, is here;
2. Be still, for the glo - ry of the Lord is shin - ing all a - round;
3. Be still, for the pow - er of the Lord is mov - ing in this place:

come bow be - fore him now with re - ver - ence and fear:
he burns with ho - ly fire, with splen - dour he is crowned:
he comes to cleanse and heal, to mi - ni - ster his grace-

in him no sin is found- we stand on ho - ly ground.
how awe - some is the sight- our rad - iant king of light!
no work too hard for him. In faith re - ceive from him.

Be still, for the pre-sence of the Lord, the ho - ly One, is here.
Be still, for the glo - ry of the Lord is shin - ing all a - round.
Be still, for the pow - er of the Lord is mov - ing in this place.

9 **Behold The Lord**

Noel Richards & Gerald Coates
Arr. Leon Evans

10   **Blessed Assurance**

Words: Fanny J. Crosby
Music: Phoebe P. Knapp

1. Bless - èd as - sur - ance, Je - sus is mine!____ Oh, what a fore - taste of glo - ry di - vine____ heir of sal - va - tion, pur - chase of God,____ born of his Spi - rit, washed in his blood!____

2. Per - fect sub - mis - sion, per - fect de - light,____ vi - sions of rap - ture now burst on my sight;____ an - gels de - scend - ing, bring from a - bove____ ech - oes of mer - cy, whis - pers of love.____ This is my

3. Per - fect sub - mis - sion, all is at rest,____ I in my sa - viour am hap - py and blessed;____ watch - ing and wait - ing, look - ing a - bove,____ filled with his good - ness, lost in his love.____

11 Breathe On Me Breath Of God

Words: Edwin Hatch
in this version Jubilate Hymns
Music: Robert Jackson Arr. Roger Mayor

Flowing ♩ = 100

1. Breathe on me, breath of God: fill me with life a - new, that as you love, so
2. Breathe on me, breath of God, un - til my heart is pure, un - til my will is
3. Breathe on me, breath of God; ful - fil my heart's de - sire, un - til this earth - ly
4. Breathe on me, breath of God; so shall I ne - ver die, but live with you the

Praying for strength

from Galatians 5

Lord, we want to control the

desires of our sinful nature:

help us to live by the Spirit.

Lord, we are weak and cannot do

as we would, but we want to

defeat

our temptations:

send your Spirit to strengthen

us.

Lord, we want to be free from

slavery to sin:

by your Spirit lead us out.

Lord, we want to inherit your

kingdom:

let your Spirit bear fruit in us.

Amen.

12 By His Grace

Steve Fry

By his grace I am re - deemed, by his blood I am made clean, and I now can know him face to face. By his power I have been raised: hid-den now in Christ by faith, I will praise the glo - ry of his grace.

13 By Your Side

Noel & Tricia Richards

Tenderly ♩ = 95

By your side I would stay,

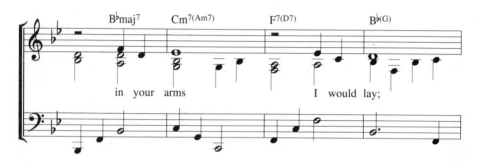

in your arms I would lay;

Je - sus, lo - ver of my soul,

no - thing from you I with - hold.

Lord, I love you and a-dore you.

What more can I say? You cause my love to grow strong-er

with ev-ery pass - ing day. day.

14 Called To A Battle
(Thunder In The Skies)

Noel & Tricia Richards
Arr. Ian Hannah

1. Called to a bat - tle- hea - ven - ly war, though we may strug - gle vic - to - ry is sure; death will not tri - umph, though we may die; Je - sus has prom - ised
2. Stand - ing to - ge - ther, mov - ing as one, we are God's ar - my called to o - ver - come; we are com - mis - sioned - Je - sus says: go, in ev - ery na - tion

15 Clap Your Hands All You Nations

Brightly ♩ = 120

John Bell

1. Clap your hands all you na - tions,
2. God sub - dues ev - ery na - tion,
3. To the shout - ing in tri - umph, A - men. _ Hal - le - lu - jah!
4. Praise the Lord with your sing - ing,
5. Those on earth who are might - y,

shout for joy all you peo - ple;
God is king of all crea - tures;
to the blast - ing of trum - pets, A - men. _ Hal - le - lu - jah!
sing God psalms _ for ev - er.
still be - long to our ma - ker,

Ho - ly is the most high;
God has giv - en this land
God _ has _ gone up, A - men. Hal - le - lu - jah!
God is mon - arch of all,
God ex - alt - ed on high,

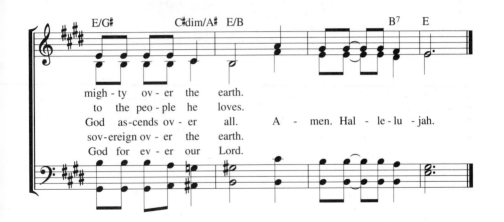

might - ty ov - er the earth.
to the peo - ple he loves.
God as-cends ov - er all. A - men. Hal - le - lu - jah.
sov-ereign ov - er the earth.
God for ev - er our Lord.

16 Closer To You

With feeling ♩ = 76

Trish Morgan

Clo-ser to you, __ Lord, and clo-ser still, __ till I am whol- ly in __ your __ will; __ clo-ser to hear __ your beat-ing heart, __ and un-der-stand __ what you __ im-part. __ O, Breath of life, __ come pu-ri-fy __ this heart of mine __ and sa-tis-fy; __

my deep de-sire___ is to wor-ship you,___ Lord of my life,___ come clo - ser still.___

Praying for grace

from Galatians 5

Lord, fill us with love, joy, peace,
patience, kindness,
goodness, faithfulness,
gentleness and self-control:
**since we live by the Spirit let us
walk in the Spirit.**

Amen.

17 Come And See
(We Worship At His Feet)

Worshipfully ♩ = 60

Graham Kendrick

1. Come and see, come and see, come and see the King of love; see the
2. Come and weep, come and mourn, for your sin that pierced him there; so much
3. Man of heaven, born to earth to re-store us to your heaven: here we

pur - ple robe and crown of thorns he wears. Sol - diers
deep - er than the wounds of thorn and nail. All our
bow in awe be - neath your search - ing eyes. From your

mock, ru - lers sneer, as he lifts the cru - el cross; lone and
pride, all our greed, all our fall - en - ness and shame- and the
tears come our joy, from your death our life shall spring; by your

friend - less now he climbs to - wards the hill.
Lord has laid the pun - ish - ment on him. We
re - sur - rec - tion po - wer we shall rise!

18   Come Let Us Sing

From Psalms 95 & 96
Sally Thornton

1. Come, let us sing for joy to the Lord, come, let us sing for joy to the Lord,

D.S. al Coda

glo - ry due his __ name, __ a - scribe to the __ Lord __

glo - ry and __ strength. __ Let us __

song!

19   Come, O Spirit Of God

N. Haydock & M. Garda

Come, O Spi - rit of God, cause blind eyes to see; in this day, a - wa - ken our land. Come, O Spi - rit of power, breathe life through your church; come, O Lord, bring hea - ven to earth, bring hea - ven to

earth.

1. In ev-ery house____ where there is
2. In ev-ery town____ a-cross this
3. In ci-ty streets____weighed down by

sor-row,_____ reach-ing out_ to com-fort those___who mourn, ____
na-tion,_____ reach-ing out_ to heal the bro-ken hearts,____
heart-ache,_____ reach-ing out_ with grace where there_ is shame,____

de-clar-ing free-dom for the cap-tives:____
re-leas-ing pris-on-ers from the dark-ness:____
once shat-tered lives___ re-stored to whole-ness:____

we'll pro-claim_ the fa - vour of the Lord._____
we'll pro-claim_ the jus - tice of our God._____
we'll dis-play_ the splen - dour of the Lord._____

20   Counter To The Culture

♩ = 100

Jon Baker & Jon Birch

Coun-ter to the cul - ture, go-ing a-gainst the flow, _ find-ing new di-rec - tion- your king-dom is up - side-down, _ your king-dom is up - side-down, _ your king-dom is up - side-down. _

1. Jus - tice, peace___ and right-
- eous-ness-___ the pol - i -tics of___ your gov-ern - ment, ___ where the
poor are blessed ___ and the strong are weak, ___ earth is in-her - i -ted
by the meek. ___ 2. In re-
- sis - tance to the spi - rit-of-the-age, live a life - style that can

be sus-tained; __ un-der-mine __ the i-dols of tech -no-lo-gy and sci-ence- the

need for the lat - est gad-get or ap - pli - ance.

3. Wo-men and men __ have e-qual worth: __

lay down power and learn to serve! __ To give is bet-ter than

to re - ceive: __ can-cel debts, love your en - e - my. __

Affirming our faith
from Galatians 5

In faith we look forward:

What are we waiting for?
Righteousness through the Spirit.

What are we hoping for?
Righteousness from God.

What is God looking for?
Faith, shown through love.

Therefore, serve one another in love.
Amen.

Hearing the commandment to love
from Galatians 5

The whole Law is summed up in one
commandment:
"Love your neighbour as yourself."
**Lord, help us to serve one another
in love.
Amen.**

21 Crown Him With Many Crowns

Words: Matthew Bridges and Godfrey Thring
in this version Jubilate Hymns
Music: George Elvey
arr. Roger Mayor

1. Crown him with ma-ny crowns, the Lamb up-on his throne, while heaven's e-ter-nal an-them drowns all mu-sic but it's
2. Crown him the Lord of life tri-umph-ant from the grave, who rose vic-to-rious from the strife for those he came to
3. Crown him the Lord of love, who shows his hands and side - those wounds yet vi-si-ble a - bove in beau-ty glo-ri-
4. Crown him the Lord of peace - his king-dom is at hand; from pole to pole let war-fare _ cease and Christ rule ev-ery
5. Crown him the Lord of years, the po-ten-tate of time, cre-at - or of the rol-ling _ spheres in ma-jes-ty sub-

22 Did You Feel The Mountains Tremble?

Martin Smith

Did you feel the moun-tains trem-ble, __ did you hear the
o-ceans roar, when the peo-ple rose to sing of __
Je-sus Christ, the ris-en One? __
Did you feel the peo-ple trem-ble, __ did you hear the

23 Don't Let My Love Grow Cold
(Light The Fire Again)

Brian Doerkson

Don't let my love grow cold, I'm calling out, 'light the fire again.' Don't let my vision die, I'm calling out, 'light the fire again.'

24 Down The Mountain
(The River Is Here)

Andy Park

feet a - dan - cing, the ri - ver of God_ fills our hearts with _ cheer, _ the

ri - ver of God_ fills our mouths with _ laugh - ter and we re - joice_ for the

Verses 2&3
Fine

ri - ver is here. _

2. The ri - ver _ of God is teem - ing with life, _ and
3. Up to the _ moun - tain we love _ to go _ to

all who _ touch _ it can be re - vived; _ and those who _ lin - ger on
find the _ pres - ence of the _ Lord; _ a - long the _ banks _ of the

1st time D.S.
Last time D.S. al fine

this ri - ver's shore will come back _ thirst - ing _ for more of _ the Lord. The
ri - ver _ we run, we dance with _ laugh - ter, giv - ing praise to _ the Son.

25 Fairest Lord Jesus

Silesian Folk Song
Arr. David Peacock

Unhurried ♩ = 96

1. Fair - est Lord Je - sus, Lord of all cre -
2. Fair are the ri - vers, mea - dows and
3. Fair is the sun - rise, star - light and
4. All fair - est beau - ty, heav - en - ly and

a - tion, Jes - us, of God and____
for - ests clothed in the fresh green____
moon - light spread - ing their glo - ry a -
earth - ly, Je - sus, my Lord, in____

man the Son; you will I
robes of spring; Je - sus is
- cross the sky; Je - sus shines
you I see; none can be

che - rish, you will I hon - our, you
fair - er, Je - sus is pur - er, he
brigh - ter, Je - sus shines clear - er, than
near - er, fair - er or dear - er, than

are my soul's de - light and
makes the sad - dest heart to
all the heav - enly host on
you, my Sav - iour, are to

crown.____
sing.____
high.____

me.

26   Faithful One

With feeling ♩ = 96

Brian Doerkson

Faith - ful One, so un - chang - ing;___ age - less One, you're my rock___ of ___ peace. ___ Lord of all, I de - pend on you, I call out to

when I___ fall down; all through_the storm___ your___ love is the_ an - chor - my___ hope is in_____ you___ a - lone.

Praying for God's renewing
from Isaiah 40

Lord, everlasting God,
creator of the ends of the earth,
you never grow tired or weary and
no-one can fathom your wisdom:
when we feel weak
increase in us your power,
when we are tired refresh us,
when we stumble and fall lift us up.
Lord, you are our hope:
renew us and strengthen us
now and always.
Amen.

Asking for God's blessing
from Isaiah 57

The Lord look upon your need and
heal you; the Lord guide you,
the Lord restore comfort to you,
the Lord give you peace.
Amen.

27 Father God

Dave Bilbrough

Worshipfully ♩ = 80

1. Fa - ther God, fill this place
(2) come with your peace,

with your love, with your grace;
heal our wounds, bring re - lease;

as we call on your name,
Lord, we long for your touch,

vis - it us in power a - gain. 2. Spi - rit,
fill our hearts with your love.

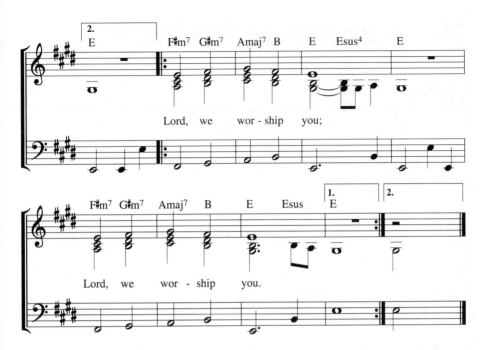

Lord, we wor - ship you;

Lord, we wor - ship you.

Greeting each other

from Galatians 1

Grace and peace to you from
God our Father and the
Lord Jesus Christ:
**to God be glory
for ever and ever!**

Amen.

28　Father Hear Our Prayer

Andy Piercy
Arr. Alison Berry

Meditatively ♩ = 100

Fa-ther, hear our prayer that our lives may be con-se-cra-ted on-ly un-to you. Cleanse us with your fire, fill us with your power that the world may glo-ri-fy your name.

Lord, have mer - cy on us.

Christ, have mer - cy on us.

Lord, have mer - cy on us.

The Lord's Prayer

from Matthew 6 and Luke 11

Our Father in heaven,

hallowed be your name,

your kingdom come,

your will be done,

on earth as it is in heaven.

Give us today our daily bread.

Forgive us our sins

as we forgive those who sin against us.

Lead us not into temptation

but deliver us from evil.

For the kingdom, the power

and the glory are yours,

now and for ever. Amen.

29 Father In Heaven, Grant To Your Children

Words: D. T. Niles
Music: Elena G. Maquiso
Arr. Geoff Weaver

1. Fa - ther in hea - ven, ___ grant to your child - ren ___ mer - cy and
(2) - deem - er, ___ may we re - mem - ber ___ your gra - cious
(3) - cend - ing, ___ whose is the bles - sing - ___ strength for the

bless - ing, ___ songs ne - ver ceas - ing; ___ love to u -
pas - sion, ___ your re - sur - rec - tion; ___ wor - ship we
wea - ry, ___ help for the nee - dy: ___ seal - ing Christ's

nite us, ___ grace to re - deem us, ___ Fa - ther in
bring you, ___ praise we shall sing you, ___ Je - sus re -
Lord - ship, ___ bless - ing our wor - ship, ___ Spi - rit des -

hea - ven, ___ Fa - ther, our God. 2. Je - sus re -
- deem - er, ___ Je - sus, our Lord. 3. Spi - rit des -
- cend - ing, ___ Spi - rit a - - dored.

30

Father In Heaven, How We Love You
(Blessed Be The Lord God Almighty)

Bob Fitts
Arr. G. Baker

Fa-ther in hea-ven, how __ we love you: _____ we
lift your name in all the earth. _____ May your
king-dom __ be es-tab-lished __ in our prais-es _____ as your
peo-ple __ de-clare your migh-ty works. __ Bless-ed be the
Lord God al-migh-ty _____ who

31 Father We Ask Of You

1. Fa-ther, we ask of you this day:___ come and heal___ our
2. Now is the time for you and I___ to join our hearts___ in

land; knit our hearts to-geth-er___ that your
praise, that the name of Je-sus___ will be

glo-ry might be seen___ in us-___ then the world___ will know that
lift-ed high___ a-bove___ the earth-___ then the world___ will know that

Je-sus Christ is Lord!___ Let us be one voice___ that
Je-sus Christ is Lord!___

32 Father You Are The Perfect Parent

Jon Birch
Arr. Ruth Spencer

Fa - ther____ you are the per - fect par - ent-___ you de - light in my tri - umphs, ___ you un - der - stand my fail - ures.___ Fa - ther,___ when I face doubts with - in, ___ Fa - ther,___ when I'm

33 Filled With Compassion
(For All The People Who Live On The Earth)

Noel & Tricia Richards
Arr. L Hills

♩ = 105
Capo 1 (G)

A♭ B♭m⁷ A♭/C D♭ A♭/C E♭ E♭⁷ A♭
(G) (Am⁷) (G/B) (C) (G/B) (D) (D⁷) (G)

1. Filled with com - pas - sion for all cre - a - tion,
2. Great is your pas - sion for all the peo - ple,
3. From ev - ery na - tion we shall be gath - ered,

B♭m⁷ A♭/C D♭ A♭/C E♭
(Am⁷) (G/B) (C) (G/B) (D)

Je - sus came in - to a world that was lost:
liv - ing and dy - ing with - out know - ing you;
mil - lions re - deemed shall be Je - sus' re - ward;

A♭ B♭m⁷ A♭/C D♭ A♭/C E♭ E♭⁷ A♭
(G) (Am⁷) (G/B) (C) (G/B) (D) (D⁷) (G)

There was but one way that he could save us,
hav - ing no sa - viour, they're lost for ev - er
then he will turn and say to his fa - ther,

B♭m⁷ A♭/C D♭ A♭/C E♭ A♭ B♭m⁷ A♭/C
(Am⁷) G/B (C) (G/B) (D) (G) (Am⁷) (G/B)

on - ly through suf - fer - ing death on a cross.
if we don't speak out and lead them to you.
'tru - ly my suf - fer - ing was worth it all.'

34 For The Joys And For The Sorrows

(For This I Have Jesus)

Graham Kendrick

1. For the joys and for the sorrows - the best and worst of times, for this moment, for to-mor-row, for all that lies be-hind; fears that crowd a-round me, for the fail-ure of my plans, for the

2. For the tears that flow in se-cret, in the bro-ken times, for the mom-ents of e-la-tion, or the troub-led mind; for all the dis-ap-point-ments, or the sting of old re-grets-

3. For the weak-ness of my bo-dy, the bur-dens of each day, for the nights of doubt and wor-ry when sleep has fled a-way; need-ing re-as-sur-ance and the will to start a-gain- a

35 Friend Of Sinners

Matt Redman

1. Friend of sin-ners, Lord of truth, I am fall-ing in __ love with you;
2. Friend of sin-ners, Lord of truth, I am giv-ing my __ life to you;

friend of sin-ners, Lord of truth, I have fall-en in __ love with you. Je-
friend of sin-ners, Lord of truth, I have giv-en my __ life to you. Je-

sus, I love __ your __ name, the __ name by

which __ we're __ saved; Je - sus, I love __ your __ name, the __

name by which __ we're __ saved.

36 From Heaven You Came

Graham Kendrick
Arr. Geoff Baker

Worshipfully ♩ = 80

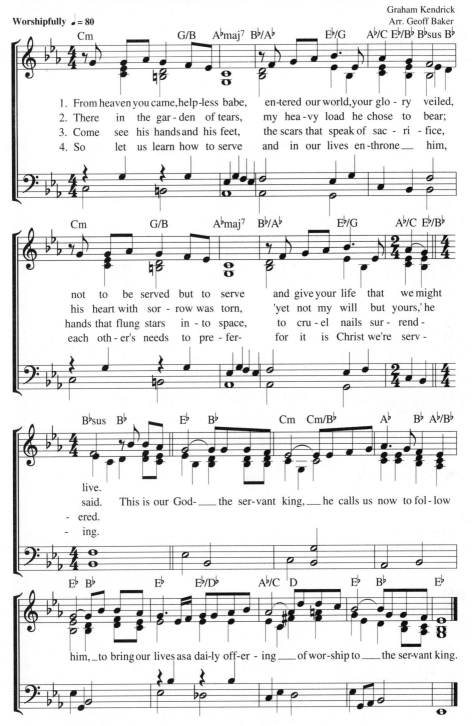

1. From heaven you came, help-less babe, en-tered our world, your glo - ry veiled,
2. There in the gar - den of tears, my hea - vy load he chose to bear;
3. Come see his hands and his feet, the scars that speak of sac - ri - fice,
4. So let us learn how to serve and in our lives en-throne ___ him,

not to be served but to serve and give your life that we might
his heart with sor - row was torn, 'yet not my will but yours,' he
hands that flung stars in - to space, to cru - el nails sur - rend -
each oth - er's needs to pre - fer- for it is Christ we're serv -

live.
said. This is our God- ___ the ser-vant king, ___ he calls us now to fol-low
- ered.
- ing.

him, _ to bring our lives as a dai-ly off-er - ing ___ of wor-ship to ___ the ser-vant king.

Affirming our faith

from Galatians 2

We are justified by faith in Jesus Christs:

We have been crucified with Christ

and we no longer live,

but Christ lives in us.

The life we now live,

we live by faith in the Son of God

who loved us and gave himself for us. Amen.

37 Glorious Things Of You Are Spoken

Words: John Newton
Croatian folk tune
Arr. Christopher Norton

Steadily ♩ = 116

1. Glo - rious things of you are spo - ken,
2. See, the streams of li - ving wa - ters,
3. Round each hab - i - ta - tion hov- er - ing,
4. Sav - iour, since of Zi - on's ci - ty

Zi - on, ci - ty of our__ God; he whose word can-
spring - ing from e - ter - nal__ love! well sup - ply our
see the cloud and fire ap - pear for a glo - ry
I, through grace, a mem - ber__ am, let the world de-

sure re - pose? with sal - va - tion's
thirst to assuage? grace, which like the
when they cry, let him hear the
pomp and show; so - lid joys and

walls sur - round - ed, you may__ smile__ at__
Lord, the gi - ver, ne - ver__ fails__ from__
loud ho - san - na ri - sing__ to__ his__
last - ing trea - sures none but__ Zi - on's__

all your__ foes.
age to__ age.
throne on__ high.
child -ren__ know.

38 Go Forth And Tell

Words: James Seddon
Music: Michael Baughen
Arr. Christopher Norton

Brightly ♩ = 132

1. Go forth and tell! O church of God, a - wake!
2. Go forth and tell! God's love em - bra - ces all;
3. Go forth and tell! Where still the dark - ness lies,
4. Go forth and tell! The doors are o - pen wide:
5. Go forth and tell! O church of God, a - rise!

God's sav - ing news to all the na - tions
he will in grace re - spond to all who
in wealth or want, the sin - ner sure - ly
share God's good gifts - let no - one be de -
go in the strength which Christ your Lord sup -

Receiving God's blessing

from Galatians 5

God has set you free: stand firm,

do not return to slavery;

and the blessing of God almighty,

Father, Son and Holy Spirit

remain with you always.

Amen.

39 God Be In My Head

Words: R. Pynson
Music: Andy Piercy
Arr. Alison Berry

With Strong Rhythm ♩ = 130

40 God Is Our Refuge And Our Strength

From Psalm 46
Dave Clifton
Arr. Alison Berry

Slow 2 ♩ = 66

God is our re-fuge and our strength, an

ev - er-pre - sent help in times of trou - ble.

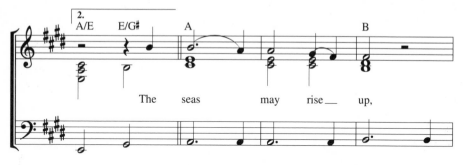

The seas may rise___ up,

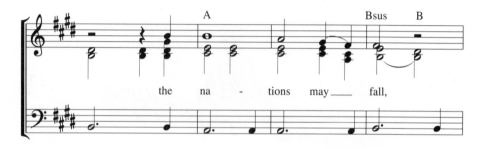

the na - tions may___ fall,

41 God Will Make A Way

God will make a way where there seems to be no way; he works in ways we can-not see, he will make a way for me. He will be my guide, hold me close-ly to his side, with

hea - ven and earth___ will fade, ___ but his word will still ___ re - main, ___ he will do ___ some - thing new ___ to - day. _____

D.S. al Fine

Blessing

May the peace of the Lord Christ go with you,
wherever He may send you,
May he guide you through the wilderness,
protect you through the storm.
May he bring you home rejoicing
at the wonders he has shown you.
May he bring you home rejoicing
once again into our doors.

42 Great Is The Darkness

(Come, Lord Jesus)

Noel Richards & Gerald Coates
Arr. Leon Evans

With strength ♩ = 140

1. Great is___ the dark-ness___ that cov-ers___ the earth, op-pres-sion,___ in-jus-tice___ and pain; na-tions___ are slip-ping___ in hope-less___ de-spair, though ma-ny___ have

2. May now___ your church rise___ with pow-er___ and love, this glo-ri-ous gos-pel___ pro-claim; in ev-ery na-tion___ sal-va-tion___ will come to those who___ be-

3. Great ce-le-bra-tions___ on that fi-nal day, when out of___ the hea-vens___ you come; dark-ness___ will van-ish,___ all sor-row___ will end, and ru-lers___ will

come in___ your name-
-lieve in___ your name.
bow at___ your throne;

watch - ing___ while san - i - ty dies,
Help us___ bring light to this world,
our great___ com - mis - sion___ com - plete,

touched by___ the mad - ness___ and lies.___
that we___ might speed your___ re - turn.___
then face___ to face we___ shall meet.___

Come, Lord Je - sus, come, Lord Je - sus,

pour out___ your Spi - rit___ we pray;

come, Lord Je - sus, come, Lord Je - sus,

pour out___ your Spi - rit on us to - day.___

43 Great Is The Lord

Steve McEwan

Great _____ is the Lord _ and most wor-thy of praise, the

ci-ty of our God, the ho-ly place, the joy of the _ whole earth

_ Great _____ is the

Lord, in whom we have _ the vic-to-ry! _ He

aids us a-gainst _ the en-e-my- we bow down on _ our knees.

And Lord, we want to lift your name on high, and Lord, we want to thank you for the works you've done in our lives; and Lord, we trust in your un-fail-ing love, for you a-lone are God e-ter-nal through-out earth and hea-ven a-bove.

44 Great Is Your Faithfulness

Words: Thomas Chisholm
in this version Jubilate Hymns
Music: William Runyan
Arr. Roger Mayor

1. Great is your faith-ful-ness, O God my Fath-er,
   you have ful-filled all your pro-mise to me;
   you ne-ver fail and your love is un-chang-ing-
   all you have been, you for ev-er will be.

2. Sum-mer and win-ter, and spring-time and har-vest,
   sun, moon and stars in their cour-ses a-bove
   join with all na-ture in e-lo-quent wit-ness
   to your great faith-ful-ness, mer-cy and love.

3. Par-don for sin, and a peace ev-er-last-ing,
   your liv-ing pre-sence to cheer and to guide;
   strength for to-day and bright hope for to-mor-row-
   these are the bless-ings your love will pro-vide.

Affirming our faith

from Galatians 5

Freedom is ours:
Christ has set us free.
Alleluia! Amen.

45 Have You Heard The Good News

Stuart Garrard

Have you ___ heard the good ___ news, ___ have you ___ heard the good ___ news? ___ We can ___ live ___ in ___ hope ___ ___ be-cause of ___ what the ___ Lord ___ has ___ done. ___ Have you ___ ___

1. There is a ___ way ___ when there ___ seems ___
2. A hope for ___ jus - tice

46 He Brought Me To His Banqueting Table
(His Banner Over Me)

Song of Songs 2:4
Kevin Prosch

o-ver me _____ is

o-ver me _____ is

love. _____

love. _____

I am my be-lov-èd's and he is mine, ___

I am my be-lov-èd's and he is mine, ___

yes, I am my be-lov-èd's and

And we can feel the love __ of God __ in this place: we be-
- lieve your good-ness, we re-ceive your grace; we de-light our-selves __ at your
ta-ble, O God, __ you do all things well- __ just look at our lives. __

MEN: He

47 He Has Risen

Noel & Tricia Richards,
& Gerald Coates
Arr. Ian Hannah

With strength ♩ = 137

He has ri - sen, he has ri - sen,

he has ri - sen, Je - sus is a - live.

Fine

When the life flowed from his bo - dy-
In the grave God did not leave him
If there were no res - ur - rec - tion,
When the Lord rides out of hea - ven,

seemed like Je - sus' miss - ion failed,
for his bo - dy to de - cay;
we our - selves could not be raised;
migh - ty an - gels at his side,

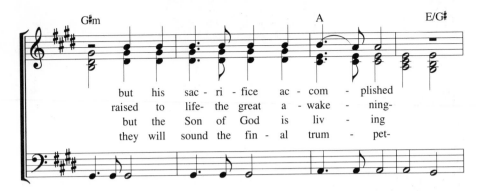

but his sac - ri - fice ac - com - plished
raised to life- the great a - wake - ning-
but the Son of God is liv - ing
they will sound the fin - al trum - pet-

vict - ory ov - er sin and hell. _____
Sa - tan's power he ov - er - came. _____
so our hope is not in vain. _____
from the grave we shall a - rise. _____

5. He has given life immortal,
   we shall see him face to face;
   through eternity we'll praise him,
   Christ the champion of our faith.

Giving God the glory

from Galatians 1

Glory be to our Lord Jesus Christ
who gave himself for our sins
to rescue us from the present evil age,
according to the will of our God and
Father,
to whom be glory
for ever and ever.
Amen.

48

He Is Exalted
The King Is Exalted On High

Flowing ♩. = 65

Twila Paris

49 He Is The Lord
(Show Your Power)

Kevin Prosch

50 Heart And Soul

Andy Thornton
Arr. Ruth Spencer

51 Here Is Love

Words: after William Rees
William Edwards
Music: Robert Lowry
Arr. Roger Mayor

Thoughtfully ♩ = 90

1. Here is love vast as the o-cean,— lov-ing kind-ness as the flood,
2. On the mount of cru - ci - fix - ion— foun-tains o - pened deep and wide;

when the Prince of life, our ran - som,— shed for us his pre - cious blood.
through the flood - gates of God's mer - cy — flowed a vast and gra - cious tide.

Who his love will not re-mem - ber;— who can cease to sing his praise?
Grace and love, like migh-ty ri - vers,— poured in-cess-ant from a - bove;

He can nev - er be for-got - ten —through-out heaven's e - ter-nal days.
and heaven's peace and per-fect jus - tice— kissed a guil-ty world in love.

52   Here We Stand In Total

C Groves & A Piercy
Arr. Alison Berry

With Drive ♩ = 65

1. Here we stand _____ in to - tal sur-

-ren - der, _____ lift - ing our voic - es _____ a - ban - doned to your

cause; here we stand, _____ pray - ing in the

glo - ry _____ of the one and on - ly _____ Je - sus Christ, the Lord.

This time-re - vi - val; _____ Lord, come and heal _

_our land, _____ bring to com - ple - tion _ the work that you've _ be-gun.

This time- re - vi - val; _____ stir up your

church a - gain, _____ pour out your Spi - rit _ on your daugh-ters and _ your sons. _

2. Here we stand _____ in need of your

53 Holy Holy

From Isaiah 6 & Rev. 4
Nathan Fellingham

Ho - ly, ___ ho - ly, ho - ly is the Lord God al - might - ty, ___ who was and is and is to come, who was and is and is to come. Lift up his name ___ with the sound of sing-

-ing, lift up his name ___ in ___ all the earth; ___

lift up your voice ___ and ___ give him glo - ry, for

he is wor - thy to ___ be ___ praised. ___

To end

54 How Firm A Foundation

Words: Richard Keen
in this version Jubilate Hymns
Music: Welsh melody
Arr. David Peacock

1. How firm a foun - da - tion, you peo - ple of God, is laid for your faith in his ex - cel - lent
2. Since Je - sus is with you, do not be a - fraid; since he is your Lord, you need not be dis -
3. When through the deep wa - ters he calls you to go, the riv - ers of trou - ble shall not ov - er -
4. When through fi - ery tri - als your path - way shall lead, his grace shall sus - tain you with all that you
5. Who - ev - er has come to be - lieve in his name will not be de - sert - ed, and not put to

55 How Good And How Pleasant

From Psalm 133
Graham Kendrick

1. How good and how plea-sant__ it is__ when we__ all live__ in u-ni-ty-__ re- -fresh - ing as dew at __ the dawn, __ like rare a-noint - ing oil____ up-on__ the head. __

2. How deep are the riv - ers__ that run__ when we__ are one__ in Je - sus__ and share with the Fa - ther__ and Son __ the bles - sings of__ his ev - er - last - ing life.__

56 How Lovely Is Thy Dwelling Place

Psalm 84
Traditional Scottish Melody
Arr. Jill Sutheran

1 & 4. How
2. E -
3. And I'd

love - ly is___ thy___ dwell-ing___ place, O___
-ven the spar - row___ finds a___ home where___
ra - ther be___ a___ door keep - er and___

Lord of hosts, to___ me; My soul is
she can set - tle___ down, and the swal - low
on - ly stay a___ day than live the

is_____ thy_____ dwell - ing____ place   O_____
those   who   are_____ dwell - ing____ where   the_____
thing_____ does_____ he   with   -   hold   from____

Lord   of   hosts   to__ me._____
song   of   praise   is__ sung._____
those   who   walk   his__ way._____

134

Canticle

Christ as a light
Illuminate and guide me
Christ as a shield
Overshadow me
Christ under me
Christ over me
Christ beside me
On my left and my right
This day be within and
Without me
Lowly and meek yet
All-powerful

Be in the heart
Of each to whom I speak
In the mouth of each
Who speaks unto me
This day be within and
Without me
Lowly and meek yet
All-powerful
Christ as a light
Christ as a shield
Christ beside me
On my left and my right.

57 How Wonderful

As a jig ♩ = 126

Dave Bilbrough

How___ won - der -ful,___ how___ glo - ri -ous___ is___ the love of___ God,___ bring - ing___ heal - ing,___ for - give - ness -___ won - der - ful love!

Let ce - le - bra - tion___ e - cho
We pro - claim_____ the king - dom___ of our
List - en to the mu - sic___ as his

through ____ this ___ land: ___ we bring re - con - ci - li - a -
God _____ is ___ here: ___ come and join __ the heaven - ly an -
prais - es fill _ the ___ air; ____ with joy _____ and with glad-

\- tion, __ we bring hope ____ to ev - ery one. __ How __
\- them __ ring - ing loud ____ and ring - ing clear. _
\- ness __ tell the peo - ple ev - ery-where: _

58 I Believe

Andy Thornton & Doug Gay
Arr. Ruth Spencer

Em
1. I be-lieve in God, the Fa - ther al - migh - ty, I be-
2. I be-lieve in Je - sus, teach - er and heal - er, I be-
3. I be-lieve the ho - ly life - giv-ing Spi - rit is a
4. I be-lieve that Je - sus died___ and was bur - ied, I be-
5. I be-lieve that he will come___ back in glo - ry, I be-

A
- lieve that he made the earth___ and___ heav - ens;___
- lieve that his life was poor___ and___ sim - ple;___
gift of the Son and Fa - ther to us;___
- lieve that he rose to life___ a - gain;___
- lieve he will judge the dead___ and liv - ing;___

Em
I be-lieve in Je - sus, born___ of a wo - man, I be-
I be-lieve he died be - trayed___ and re - ject - ed, I be-
I be-lieve the three are one___ and un - it - ed, I be-
I be-lieve that he was tak - en to hea - ven, I be-
I be-lieve the res - ur - rec - tion of bo - dy, I be-

A   1.-5.   D.S. al Fine
- lieve that he is the Son___ of God. I be - lieve.
- lieve that he fought the power___ of ev - il. I be - lieve.
- lieve in his heal- ing and___ for - give-ness. I be - lieve.
- lieve that he reigns at God's___ right hand. I be - lieve.
- lieve in the life that's ev - er - last - ing. I be - lieve.

59 I Give You All The Honour

1 Chron 16:25-27
Luke 4:18-21
Carl Tuttle

1. I give you all the hon-our____ and praise that's due your name:
   Spi - rit moves up - on me now,__ you meet my deep-est need;
   bro - ken chains that bound me,__ you've set this cap-tive free;

   for you are the King of glo - ry,____ the cre-a - tor of all things. ____
   and I lift my hands up to your throne-__ your mer-cy I've re-ceived. ____ And I
   I will lift my voice to praise your name__ for all e - ter-ni-ty. ____

   wor - ship you,____ I give my life to you,____

60 I Have Felt The Wind Blow

Brian Doerkson

C

___ a might - y___ tree, the vast___ ex - panse ___
- den fields___ of___ grain 'neath end - less___ blue ___
___ a might - y___ tree, the vast___ ex - panse ___

F   1.,2.

___ of o - pen___ sea?_____
___ hor - i - zon's___ frame._____
___ of o - pen___ sea?_____

C

3. F   D.S.

2. Gaz - ing at a   I love to stand___
3. Liste - ning to a

Affirming our faith

from Isaiah 44

We believe in one God
who made all things:
he alone stretched out the heavens
and spread out the earth;
he formed us in the womb,
he is our king and our redeemer -
the Lord almighty.

We belong to the Lord -
we are his people,
we are called by his name;
he pours out his Spirit upon us
as water on a thirsty land:
we believe in one God, the almighty,
Father, Son and Holy Spirit.
Amen

61 I Lift My Eyes Up

From Psalm 121
Brian Doerksen

I lift my eyes up to the moun-tains: where does my help come from? My help comes from you, Mak-er of hea-ven, Cre-a-tor of the earth. earth. Oh, how I need you Lord- you are my on-ly hope,_ you're my on-ly

prayer; so, I will wait for you to come and res-cue me,

come and give me life.

For God's blessing
from Philippians 4

O Lord,
open our eyes to see what is beautiful,
our minds to know what is true,
and our hearts to love what is good;
for Jesus' sake.

Amen.

62   I See The Lord Exalted

From Isaiah 6
John Chisum & Don Moen

63

I See The Lord

From Isaiah 6
Chris Falson

I see the_ Lord_ seat-ed_ on_ the_throne-_ ex-alt-ed;_ and the train of his_ robe_ fills the_tem - ple_ with glo - ry: the whole earth_ is_ fill-ed, the whole earth_ is_ filled,_ the

64 I The Lord Of Sea And Sky

(Here I Am, Lord)

Isaiah 6
Daniel Schutte

♩ = 96

1. I, the Lord of sea and sky, I have heard my peo-ple cry;
2. I, the Lord of snow and rain, I have borne my peo-ple's pain;
3. I, the Lord of wind and flame, I will tend the poor and lame,

all who dwell in dark and sin my hand will save.
I have wept for love of them- they turn a-way.
I will set a feast for them- my hand will save.

I, who made the stars of night, I will make their dark-ness bright.
I will break their hearts of stone, give them hearts for love a-lone;
Fin-est bread I will pro-vide till their hearts are sa-tis-fied;

Who will bear my light to them? Whom shall I send?
I will speak my word to them. Whom shall I send?
I will give my life to them. Whom shall I send?

65   I Walk By Faith

Blues/Rock ♩ = 152

Chris Falson

I walk by faith, each step by faith; to live by faith I put my trust in___ you. I

is — a prayer of faith- — and if my God is for —

— me — then who can be a-gainst — me? — I

D.S. al Fine

Praise response

from Psalm 107

Give thanks to God, for he is good;
his love endures for ever.

Let those whom the Lord has redeemed
repeat these words of praise:
**O thank the Lord for his love and the
wonderful things he has done! Amen.**

66 I Want To Be Out Of My Depth In Your Love

Gently ♩ = 100

Doug Horley

I want to be out of my depth in your love,
feel-ing your arms so strong a-round me;
out of my depth in your love,
out of my depth in you. I want to be

Learn-ing to let ___ you lead, ___ put - ting all trust ___
Things I have held ___ so tight, ___ made my se - cu -

___ in you; ___ deep- er in - to ___ your arms, ___
- ri - ty; ___ give me the strength ___ I need ___

1.
sur - round-ed by you.
2.
to sim - ply let go. ___

67 I Will Cry Mercy

♩ = 70

Sue Rinaldi & Steve Bassett
Arr. Stuart Townend

passion melt my heart of stone; let your beauty be seen in my life; let your heart-beat be my own._____ So I'll cry mercy for this nation, let us see healing for the people; and I'll cry justice for this nation,____ O God.

68   I Will Offer Up My Life

Matt Redman

1. I will of-fer up my life in spi-rit and truth,
pour-ing out the oil of love as my wor-ship to you.
In sur-ren-der I must

2. You de-serve my ev-ery breath for you've paid the great cost-
giv-ing up your life to death, ev-en death on a cross.
You took all my shame a-

Canticle

Teach us, dear Lord

to number our days

That we may apply

our hearts unto wisdom

Oh, satisfy us early

with thy mercy

That we may rejoice

and be glad all of our days

And let the beauty of the Lord

our God be upon us

And establish Thou

the work of our hands

And let the beauty of the Lord

our God be upon us

And establish Thou

the work of our hands, dear Lord

69 I Will Sing The Wondrous Story

Words: F.H. Rawley
Music: R.H. Prichard

70   I Will Speak Out

Ray Goudie, Steve Bassett
Dave Bankhead & Sue Rinaldi

I will speak out for those who have no voi - ces,
I will speak out for those who have no choi - ces,

I will stand up for the rights of all the op-pressed,
I will cry out for those who live with-out love,

— I will speak truth and jus - tice, I'll de-
— I will show God's com - pas - sion to the

fend the poor and the need - y, I will lift up__ the__
crushed and bro - ken in spi - rit, I will lift up__ the__

weak in Je - sus' name.
weak in Je - sus'

name,_____ in Je - sus' name.

71   I Will Wait

Maggi Dawn

I will ___ wait for your peace ___ to come ___ to me, ___

I will ___ wait for your peace ___ to come ___ to me; ___

— and I'll sing ___ in the dark - ness, ___ and I'll

wait with-out fear, ___ and I'll sing ___ in the dark-

- ness, ___ and I'll wait with-out fear. ___

I Will Worship

David Ruis

all my __ wor - ship, I will give __ you all my __ praise; _____

__ you a-lone __ I long to __ wor - ship, you a-lone __ are

wor - thy __ of __ my _____ praise. _____

73 I Worship You, Almighty God

Ex 15:11, Ps 71:19
Sandra Corbett

74 I'm Standing On The Rock

Straight rock ♩ = 144

Chris Falson

I'm stand - ing on the rock, and my name is on the roll, wo - ah- I'm a be - liev - er! He's the rock of all ag - es, he's the shep - herd of my soul, wo - ah- I'm a be - liev - er!

I be-lieve in the ris-en Lord___ seat-ed on___the throne,___ cast-ing down___ the strong-holds of the en-e-my.___ He's the first of all___ cre-a-tion,___ the be-gin-ning and___ the end,___ let the earth___ pro-claim,___ 'there's sal-va-tion in___ his name!'___

75   I'm Yours

I want to make a diff - erence — in this world. —

1.
I want to —

2.
I'm yours!

To end

D.S.
1. I'm — I'm yours!

76 Is Anyone Thirsty

With strength ♩ = 112

Graham Kendrick

Is an-y-one thirs-ty-___ an-y-one?___ Is

an-y-one thir - sty?_ Is

Je - sus said:____ 'let them come_ to me____ and drink, ___

let them come_ to me.'_____ Oh, _

let the liv-ing wa-ters flow,_ oh,_ let the liv-ing wa-

77 It Takes Faith

Jon Birch
Arr. Ruth Spencer

1. It takes faith to be-lieve in sci - ence, it takes faith to be-lieve in your health; _ it takes faith to be-lieve in mon - ey, it takes faith to be-lieve in your-self: _ but I will put my trust in You. _____ I put my faith in man - y things, I

184

put my faith in Je - sus- he will stand in my de-fence;
and right there in his pre - sence, I will
have self - con - fi - dence: yes, I will

D.S. al Fine

put my trust in You.

Psalm 23

The Lord is my shepherd,
I shall not be in want.
He makes me lie down in green pastures,
he leads me beside quiet waters,
he restores my soul.
He guides me in paths of righteousness
for his name's sake.

Even though I walk
through the valley of the
shadow of death,
I will fear no evil,
for you are with me;
your rod and your staff,
they comfort me.

78 It's Good To Be Human

Jonny Baker
Arr. R Spencer

♩ = 100

It's good to be hu-man- good to be a-live,—

li-ving in— your world;— thanks for— life! Such in-

-cred-i-ble— di-ver-si-ty,— it's good to be a-live:—

thanks for— the gift-— thanks for— life!—

good to be a-live; __ thanks for __ the gift- __ thanks for __ life! __

Sha -king off our numb - ness, sa - vour - ing __ plea - sure- the

ec- sta- sy __ of liv - ing: thanks for __ life- __ it's a gift from you!

79 It's Rising Up

Matt Redman
& Martin Smith

It's ris-ing up from coast to coast, from north to south, and east to west; the cry of hearts that love your name, which with one voice we will pro-claim. The for-mer things have ta-ken place: can

ho - ly   is___ the___ Lord!"

2. And we have___ heard___ the

Li - on's___ roar___ that speaks of___ heav - en's___ love.

_ and_ power:___ is this the _ time,___ is this the _ call___ that

80 Jesus Is The Name We Honour
(We Will Glorify)

Brightly ♩ = 140

Phil Lawson-Johnston

1. Je - sus is the name we ho - nour, ___ Je - sus is the name ___ we praise. ___ Ma - jes - tic name a - bove ___ all oth - er names; ___ the high - est heaven ___ and earth pro - claim ___ that
2. Je - sus is the name we wor - ship, ___ Je - sus is the name ___ we trust. ___ He is the King a - bove ___ all oth - er kings; ___ let all cre - a - tion stand and sing ___ that
3. Je - sus is the Fa - ther's splen - dour, ___ Je - sus is the Fa - ther's joy. ___ He will re - turn to reign ___ in ma - je - sty, ___ and ev - ery eye ___ at last shall see ___ that

81 Jesus, Jesus, Holy And Anointed One

John Barnett

With feeling ♩ = 70

Jesus, Jesus, ho-ly and an-oin-ted One, __ Je - sus.

ri - sen and ex - alt -ed One, __ Je - sus.

1st & last time — Fine

- sus: your name is like hon - ey on __ my lips, _____ your Spi-rit like wa- ter to __ my soul; __ your word is a lamp __ un - to __ my feet- __ Je - sus, I love _____ you, _____ I love __ you.

D.C. al Fine

82 Lead Me Lord

Charles Wesley
Arr. Dave Clifton & Alison Berry

Lead me, Lord, lead me in your righ - teous - ness, make your way plain be - fore my face. face. For it is you, Lord, you,___ Lord,___ on - ly that makes me to dwell in___ safe - ty.

83 Let Us Celebrate

Geoff Baker

Let us ce - le - brate his love for us, mar - vel at his
love for us- Je - sus Christ the liv - ing Word.
Mer - cy and for - give - ness free, flow - ing down through
his - tor - y- Je - sus Christ the ris - en

84 Let Us Give Thanks

Words: from The Alternative
Service Book 1980
Music: Andy Piercy
Arr. Alison Berry

With strong beat ♩ = 112

Let us give thanks to the Lord our___ God.___

It is right to give him thanks and___ praise.

thanks and___ praise. It is not on-ly___ right,___ it is our

du-ty and our joy___ it is right to give him

85 Living Lord

Charlie Groves
Arr. C. Mcleish & C. Hutchison

Li - ving Lord, I give my life to you: you're there when I call. Liv - ing Lord, I give my soul to you: my heart, my mind, my all. heart, my mind my

86 Lord Help Us Live

Geoff Baker

♩. = 50

1. Lord, help us live_____ in the light of your com - ing,
2. Lord, help us see_____ there is hope be - yond mea - sure,
3. Lord, fill our hearts_____ with a real ex - pec - ta - tion,

striv - ing for pur - i - ty, flee - ing from sin;
joy be - yond suff - er - ing, jus - tice re - stored.
heirs of the pro - mise, our des - ti - ny sealed;

Catch - ing a glimpse_____ of what we are be - com - ing,
Fix - ing our eyes_____ on the heav - en - ly trea - sure-
prais - ing our sav - iour with glad ad - or - a - tion,

be-ing trans-formed to your like-ness with - in._____
Je-sus, our sav-iour, re - deem-er and Lord._____ The
when in your glo-ry you shall be re - vealed._____

trum - pet shall sound: look to the skies, for

Je-sus is com-ing a - gain;_____ then through the clouds his

child - ren shall rise to share in his glor - i - ous reign.____

87 Lord I Lift Your Name On High

♩ = 80

Rick Founds

Lord, I lift your name on high,

Lord, I love to sing your prais - es; I'm so glad you're in my

life, I'm so glad you came to save us.

You came from hea - ven to earth to show the way,

from the earth to the cross, my debt to pay;

from the cross to the grave, from the grave to the sky,

Lord, I lift your name on high.

88 Lord Of Lords

Jessy Dixon, Randy Scruggs
& John W. Thompson

1. Lord of lords, __ King of kings, __ ma-ker of heaven __ and earth __
2. Lord, you're right-eous in all your ways, __ we bless your ho - ly name

__ and all __ good things, _____ we give you glo -
and we give __ you praise, _____ we give you glo -

- ry. __ Lord Je-ho-vah, Son of Man, __
- ry. __ You reign for ev - er in ma-je-sty-__ we

prec - ious Prince of peace and the great __ I AM, _____
praise and lift you up for e - ter - ni - ty, _____

89 Lord Pour Out Your Spirit

(Great Awakening)

Joel 2:28

R.Goudie, S.Bassett & D.Bankhead

♩ = 80

1. Lord, pour out your Spi - rit___ on all the peo - ples of the earth;_____ let your sons and daugh -ters___ speak your words of pro - phe -cy._____ Send us dreams and vi - sions, re - veal the se - cret of your heart;_____

2. Lord, pour out your Spi - rit___ on all the na -tions of the world;_____ let them see your glo - ry, ___ let them fall in rev - erent awe._____ Show your migh - ty pow - er, shake the hea - vens and the earth;_____

90 Lord We Long For You
(Heal Our Nation)

Trish Morgan, Ray Goudie
Ian Townend & Dave Bankhead

Prayerfully ♩ = 90

1. Lord, we long for you to move in pow - er;
   there's a hun - ger deep with - in our hearts
   to see heal - ing in our na - tion: send your Spi - rit to re -
   vive us -

2. Lord, we hear your Spi - rit com - ing clo - ser -
   a migh - ty wave to break up - on our land,
   bring - ing jus - tice, and for - give - ness: God, we cry to you, 'Re -
   vive us!'

Heal our na - tion,

91 Lord, You Have My Heart

Tenderly ♩ = 110

Martin Smith

Lord, you have my heart, and I will search for yours:

Je - sus, take my life and lead me
Let me be to you a sac - ri -

on.
- fice.

(MEN) And

(WOMEN) I will praise you,

I will praise you, Lord, and

Collect

Eternal God and Father,
you create us by your power
and redeem us by your love:
guide and strengthen us
by your Spirit,
that we may give ourselves
in love and service
to one another and to you;
through Jesus Christ our Lord.

Amen.

92 Love Divine, All Loves Excelling

Words: Charles Wesley
in this version Jubilate Hymns
Music: Linda Jones

1. Love di - vine _____ all loves ex -
(2) - migh - ty to de -
(3) then _____ your new cre -

- cell - ing, _____ joy of heaven _____ to
- liv - er, _____ let us all _____ your
- a - tion: _____ pure and sin - less

earth come down: fix in us _____ your
grace re - ceive; sud - den - ly _____ re -
let us be; let us see _____ your

hum - ble dwell - ing, _____ all your faith - ful
- turn, and ne - ver, _____ ne - ver more your
great sal - va - tion, _____ per - fect in e -

mer - cies____ crown.
tem - ples____ leave.
- ter - ni - ty:

Je - sus,
You we
changed from

Gmaj⁷　　　　　　**A⁷**　　　　　　**Bm⁷**

you　　　are　all　　com - pas - sion,_____
would　　be　al - ways　bless - ing,_____
glo - ry　in - to　glo - ry_____

D/A　　　　　　**Gmaj⁷**　　　　　　**A⁷**

___ bound - less　love　　that　makes　us
___ serve　you　as　　your　hosts　a -
___ till　in　heaven　we　take　our

Bm　　　　　　**F♯m**　　　　　　**Em**

whole:　　　　vis - it　us　　with
bove,　　　　pray,　and　praise　you
place,　　　　there　to　cast　our

your ... sal - va - tion, ... en - ter
with - out ceas - ing, ... glo - ry
crowns ... be - fore you, ... lost in

ev - ery trem - bling___ soul.
in ... your per - fect___ love.
won - der, love and___

1.,2.
2. Come, al - ... praise. ... praise.
3. Fin - ish

93 May Our Attitude

A. Piercy & D. Clifton
Arr. Alison Berry

With drive ♩ = 106

May our at-ti-tude __ be as that of Christ __ who, be-ing ve-ry na-ture God, __ did not con-si-der e-qual-i-ty with God some-thing to be grasped, __ but made him-self no-thing, __ tak-ing the ve-ry na-ture of a ser-vant, be-ing made __ in hu-man

224

94   Meekness And Majesty

Graham Kendrick
Arr. Chris Norton

1. Meek-ness and ma-jes-ty, man-hood and de-i-ty,
2. Fath-er's pure ra-di-ance, per-fect in in-no-cence,
3. Wis-dom un-search-a-ble, God the in-vis-i-ble,

in per-fect har-mo-ny- the man who is God:
yet learns o-be-di-ence to death on a cross:
love in-de-struct-i-ble in frail-ty ap-pears:

Lord of e-ter-ni-ty dwells in hu-man-i-ty, kneels in hu-
suff-ering to give us life, conquer-ing through sac-ri-fice- and, as they
Lord of in-fin-i-ty, stoop-ing so ten-der-ly, lifts our hu-

-mi-li-ty___ and___ wash-es our feet.
cru-ci-fy, prays,___ 'Fa-ther, for-give'. Oh, what a
-man-i-ty to the heights of his throne.

95 Men And Women Partners Together

♩ = 76

Jon Baker
Arr. R. Spencer

1. Men and wo-men,___ part-ners to-geth-er,___ made to be hu-man,___ to live in the earth;___ gi-ven a man-date___ to de-ve-lop cre-a-tion,___ un-lock its po-ten-tial and bring new things to birth.___

2. Go and be fruit-ful,___ in-crease in num-ber,___ lov-ing-ly stew-ard,___ rule and take care___ of all of God's crea-tures___ that move on the___ land-___ the fish in the___ sea and the birds of the air.___

(3) crown of cre-a-tion,___ bear-ing your im-age,___ giv-en the earth___ to shape and to mould;___ cov-en-ant part-ners,___ your___ re-pres-ent-a-tion___ as his-tory de-vel-ops and cul-ture un-folds.___

96 Men Of Faith

'Je - sus is sav - iour to all, Lord of hea - ven and

Last Time To Coda

1.,3.

2.

earth.' _____ 2. Rise up,
3. Rise up,

We've been through fire, __ we've been through rain; we've been re - fined by the

power of his name. We've fal - len deep - er in love with you—

you've burned the truth on our lips. _____

Lord of hea - ven and earth, Lord of hea - ven and

earth, Lord of hea - ven and earth.

Declaration of faith

To whom shall we go?

You have the words of eternal life,

And we have believed and have come to know

That you are the Holy One of God.

Praise to you, Lord Jesus Christ.

King of endless glory.

97 My Heart Is Full

From Hebrews 1
Graham Kendrick

Moderate ♩ = 65

mf

1. My heart is full of ad-mi-ra-tion for you, my Lord, my God and King; your ex-cel-lence, my in-spi-ra-tion, your words of grace have made my spi-rit sing. 2. You love what's

98 My Jesus I Love Thee

R. Featherstone
Music: Adoniram J. Gordon

♩ = 100

238

Gm F C/E C F F/A B♭ F/C C

-deem – er, my sav – iour art thou, _____ if
wear – ing the thorns _____ on thy brow- _____ if
glit – ter – ing crown _____ on my brow, _____ 'if

F B♭/F F C/E Dm⁷ Gm⁷ F/C C

ev – er I loved _____ thee, my Je – sus tis
ev – er I loved _____ thee, my Je – sus tis
ev – er I loved _____ thee, my Je – sus tis

1.,2.
F F/A B♭ Gm⁷ Gm⁷/C
3.
F

now.
now.
2. I
3. In
now.'

99 My Jesus, My Saviour

My Je - sus, my Sav - iour, Lord, there is none___ like___ you;___

___ all of my days___ I want to praise_____ the won - ders of your

migh - ty love. My com - fort, my shel - ter,

tow - er of ref - uge and strength,___ let ev - ery breath,___ all that I am,___

___ ne - ver cease to wor - ship you. Shout to the Lord _ all the earth,___

100 My Lips Shall Praise You

(Restorer Of My Soul)

Noel & Tricia Richards
Arr. L Evans

My lips shall praise you, my __ great re -
- deem - er; my heart will wor - ship,

Last Time To Coda

al - migh - ty Sav - iour.

1. You take all my
2. Love that con - quers
3. You're the source of

guilt a - way, turn the dark - est night to __ bright - est
ev - ery fear! In the midst of trou - ble __ you __ draw
hap - pi - ness, bring-ing peace when I am __ in __ dis-

day: you are the re - stor - er of __ my __ soul. _____
near: you are the re - stor - er of __ my __ soul. _____
- tress: you are the re - stor - er of __ my __ soul. _____

Coda

al - migh - ty Sav - iour, al - migh - ty

Sav - iour, al - migh - ty Sav - iour!

101 My Lord What Love Is This
(Amazing Love)

With strength ♩ = 130

Graham Kendrick

Lord, _____ what love is this _____ that pays _____
(2) so, _____ they watched him die, _____ des - pised, _____
(3) now _____ this love of Christ _____ shall flow _____

_ so dear - ly, _____ that I, _____ the
_ re - ject - ed; _____ but oh, _____ the
_ like ri - vers: _____ come, wash _____ your

guil - ty one, _____ may go free! _____
blood he shed _____ flowed for me! _____
guilt a - way, _____ live a - gain! _____

A - maz - ing love,_____ oh what sac - ri - fice,_____ the

Son of God_____ given for me._____ My

debt he pays_____ and my death he dies_____ that

I _____ might live,_____ that

I _____ might live._____

247

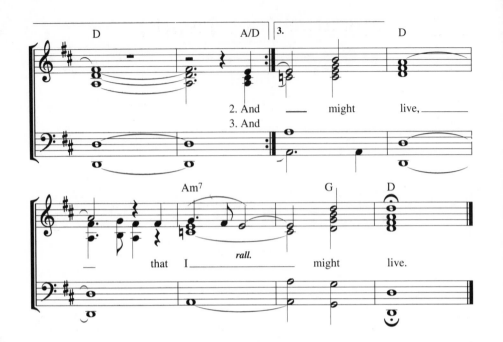

2. And —— might live,——
3. And

that I ———— might live.

rall.

102   Nothing Can Trouble

Taizé Community

No - thing can trou - ble, no - thing can frigh - ten -

those who seek God shall ne - ver go want - ing.

God a - lone fills us.

103 Nothing Shall Separate Us

Strong and bright ♩ = 115

Noel & Tricia Richards

No - thing shall se - par - ate us from the love of God,

no - thing shall se - par - ate us from the love of God.

1. God did — not spare his on - ly Son, gave him to save us — all;
2. Up from — the grave Je - sus — was raised to sit at God's right — hand;
3. Now by — God's grace we have — em - braced a life set free from — sin;

sin's price — was met by Je - sus' death and hea - ven's mer - cy — falls.
plead - ing — our cause in hea - ven's courts - for - giv - en we can — stand.
we shall — de - ny all that — de - stroys our un - i - on with — him.

104 Now Thank We All Our God

Words: after Martin Rinkhart
Catherine Winkworth
Music: Johann Crüger
Arr. Roger Mayor

1. thank we all our God with hearts and hands and voi - ces; such won - ders he has done! in

(2) may this gen - erous God through all our life be near us; to fill our hearts with joy, and

(3) praise and thanks to God who reigns in high - est hea - ven; to Fa - ther and to Son and

still is ours to - day.
this world and the next.
shall be ev - er -

2. So
3. All

- more.

105 Now To Him Who Loved Us

Words: Samuel Waring
Music: Linda Jones

Now to him _____ who loved _____ us, gave us ev- ery pledge ___ that love could give, ___ free- ly shed his blood to save _____ us, gave his life that we ___ might live, ___ be the

king-dom___ and do-min-ion_____ and the glo-ry ev-er-more,.

be the king-dom___ and do-min-ion_____ and the

1. **2.**

glo-ry ev-er-more! ___

106   O Breath Of Life

Words: Elizabeth Head
Music: Mary Hammond
Arr. Roger Mayor

1. O Breath of life, come sweep - ing through us, re - vive your church with life and
2. O Wind of God, come bend us, break us, till hum - bly we con - fess our
3. O Breath of love, come breathe with - in us, re - new - ing thought and will and

107 O Father Of The Fatherless
(Father Me)

Graham Kendrick

♩ = 100

1. O Father of the fatherless, in whom all fami-
(2) bruised and broken I draw near, you hold me close and
(3) in my foolishness I stray, returning emp-ty
(4) when I look into your eyes, from deep within my

-lies are blessed, I love the way you father me.
dry my tears, I love the way you father me.
and a-shamed, I love the way you father me.
spi-rit cries: I love the way you father me.

You gave me life, forgave the past, now
At last my fearful heart is still, sur-
Ex-changing for my wretch-ed-ness your
Be-fore such love I stand a-mazed, and

in your arms I'm safe at last- I love the way you father me.
-rend-ered to your per-fect will- I love the way you father me.
rad-iant robes of right-eous-ness- I love the way you father me.
ev-er will through end-less days- I love the way you father me.

108 O Lord The Clouds Are Gathering

Graham Kendrick

♩ = 72

1. O— Lord,— the clouds are gath - er - ing,— the fire of judg - ment burns.— How we have fal - len! O—— Lord,— you stand ap - palled to see— your laws of love so scorned— and lives so bro - ken. Have

(2) Lord,— ov - er the na - tions now,— where is the dove of peace?— Her wings are bro - ken, O—— Lord,— while pre - cious child-ren starve,— the tools of war in-crease,— their bread is sto - len. Have

(3) Lord,— dark powers are poised to flood— our streets with hate and fear.— We must a - wak - en! O—— Lord,— let love re - claim the lives— that sin would sweep a - way,— and let your king - dom come! Have

(4) Lord,— your glo - rious cross shall tower— tri - um - phant in this land,— e - vil con - found - ing; through the fire,— your suf - 'ering church dis- plays— the glo - ries of her Christ,— prais - es re - sound - ing. Have

MEN:

Affirming our faith

from Galatians 6

Through the cross of Jesus Christ:
the world has been crucified to us,
and we to the world.

In Christ there is a new creation:
nothing else counts any more. Amen.

109 O Lord Who Came From Realms Above

Words: Charles Wesley
in this version Jubilate Hymns
Music: Samuel Stanley, Arr. Roger Mayor

With life ♩ = 120

1. O Lord, who came from realms a - bove the pure - ce -
2. There let it for your glo - ry___ burn with in - ex -
3. Je - sus, con - firm my hearts de - sire to work and
4. Here let me prove your per - fect__ will, my acts of

- les - tial fire to im - part, kin - dle___ a___ flame___ of___
tin - guish - ab - le__ blaze, and trem - bling__ to___ its___
speak and think for__ you; still let___ me__ guard___ the___
faith and love re - peat, till death__ your__ end - less__

sac - cred__ love__ up - on the al - tar of my___ heart.
source__ re - turn__ in hum - ble prayer and fer - vent__ praise.
ho - ly__ fire,__ and still in me your gift re - new.
mer - cies__ seal__ and make the sac - ri - fice com - plete!

110 Only By Grace

Gerrit Gufstafson

Gently ♩ = 90

On - ly by grace__ can we en - ter,__ on - ly by grace__ can we stand; __ not by our hu - man en -dea - vour, __ but by the blood__ of the Lamb. __ In - to your pres - ence you call__ us, __ you call__ us to come; __ in - to your pres - ence you draw__ us, __ and

now by your grace_ we come,_ now by your grace_ we come._

Lord, if you mark_ our trans-gres-

-sions, who will stand?

Thanks to your grace___ we are cleansed___ by the blood___ of the Lamb._

111 Our Confidence Is In The Lord

Noel & Tricia Richards

♩ = 112

Our con - fi - dence is in the Lord, the source of our sal - va - tion. Rest is found in him a - lone, the au - thor of cre - a - tion. We will not fear the ev - il day be - cause we have a ref - uge; in ev - ery cir - cum - stance we say,

112 Our God Is Awesome In Power
(Warrior)

Rocky ♩ = 115

Noel & Tricia Richards

1. Our God is awe - some in pow - er:
2. Wa - ken the war - ri - or spi - rit:

scat - ters his en - em - ies; _____
ar - my of God - __ a - rise! _____

our God is migh - ty in bring - ing   the pow-er-ful to __ their knees. _
chall-enge the pow - ers of dark - ness -   there must be no com-prom - ise; _

—   He has put on __ his   ar - mour,
—   we shall at - tack __ their   strong - holds,

Affirming our faith

from Galatians 3

Christ redeemed us
from the curse of the law
by becoming a curse for us,
hanging upon the tree.

We are redeemed through Christ Jesus,
and by faith we receive
the promise of the Spirit.

Amen.

113 Over The Mountains And The Sea
(I Could Sing Of Your Love Forever)

Martin Smith
Arr. G Baker

O-ver the moun-tains and the sea, your ri-ver runs with love for me, and I will o-pen up my heart and let the heal-er set me free. I'm hap-py to be in the truth, and I will dai-ly lift my hands: for I will al-ways sing of when your love came down. (Yeah!)___

Chorus
I could sing of your love ___ for ___ ev - er, ___ I could sing of your love_

114 Overwhelmed By Love

With feeling ♩ = 80

Noel Richards

O - ver - whelmed by love, deep-er than
All my sin was laid on your dear

o -ceans, high as the heav - ens; ev - er - liv - ing
Son, __ your pre-cious one; __ all my debt he

God - your love has res - cued me.
paid - great is your love for me.

No -one could ev - er earn your love;

your grace and mer-cy is free._____ Lord, these

words are true - so is my love for you,

so is my love for you.

115 Praise God From Whom All Blessings Flow

Andy Piercy & Dave Clifton
Arr. Alison Berry

Steady Rock ♩ = 132

Praise God from whom all bless-ings flow, praise him all crea-tures here be-low. Praise him a-bove you hea-venly host, praise Fa-ther, Son and Ho-ly Ghost. Praise

1.,5.,7. *3rd time to bridge*
Last time to Coda

2.,4.,6.
-ly Ghost. Give glo-ry to the Fa-ther, give

glo-ry to the Son,___ give glo-ry to the Spi-rit___ while end-less a-ges run. 'Wor-thy the Lamb,'___ all hea-ven cries___ to be ex-al-ted thus;___ 'Wor-thy the Lamb,'___ our hearts___ re-ply___ for he was slain for us. Praise

Affirming our faith

from Galatians 4

When the time had fully come,
God sent his Son,
born of a woman,
born to redeem us:
We are in truth his children.

Because we are his children:
**God sent the Spirit of his Son
into our hearts.**

We are slaves no longer,
but children:
God's children and heirs.

Alleluia! Amen.

116   Praise My Soul

Words: from Psalm 103
Henry Francis Lyte
Music: John Goss
Arr. David Peacock

With strength ♩ = 102

1. Praise, my soul, the king of hea - ven; to his feet your tri - bute bring! Ran - somed, healed, re - stored, for - gi - ven,
2. Praise him for his grace and fa - vour to our fa - thers in dis - tress; praise him still the same as ev - er,
3. Fa - ther - like he tends and spares us; all our hopes and fears he knows, in his hands he gent - ly bears us,
4. An - gels, help us to a - dore him - you be - hold him face to face; sun and moon, bow down be - fore him -

who like me his praise should sing? Al - le - lu - ia,
slow to blame and swift to bless, Al - le - lu - ia,
res - cues us from all our foes, Al - le - lu - ia,
praise him, all in time and space, Al - le - lu - ia,

al - le - lu - ia! praise the ev - er - last - ing king!
al - le - lu - ia! glo - rious in his faith - ful - ness!
al - le - lu - ia! wide - ly as his mer - cy flows.
al - le - lu - ia! praise with us the

God of grace!

117 Praise To The Lord, The Almighty

Music: S. Gesangbuch
Words: J. Neander;
trans. C. Winkworth & P. Dearmer
Music arrangement by C. Groves & A. Berry

♩ = 96

1. Praise to the Lord, the al - might - y, the king of cre -
2. Praise to the Lord, who o'er all things so wonde - rous - ly
3. Praise to the Lord, who doth pros - per thy work and de -
4. Praise to the Lord, O let all that is in me a -

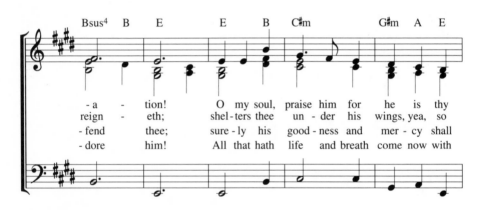

- a - tion! O my soul, praise him for he is thy
reign - eth; shel - ters thee un - der his wings, yea, so
- fend thee; sure - ly his good - ness and mer - cy shall
- dore him! All that hath life and breath come now with

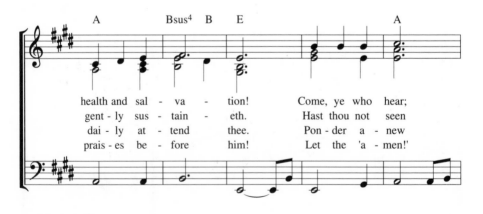

health and sal - va - tion! Come, ye who hear;
gent - ly sus - tain - eth. Hast thou not seen
dai - ly at - tend thee. Pon - der a - new
prais - es be - fore him! Let the 'a - men!'

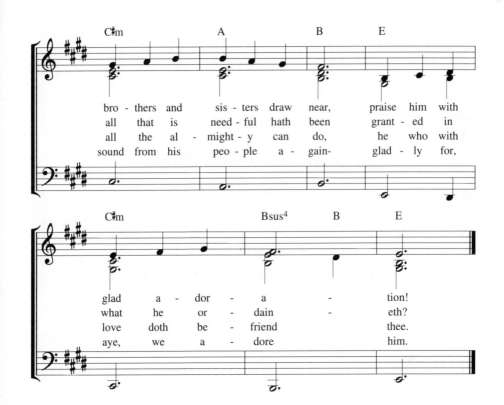

C#m   A   B   E

bro - thers and   sis - ters draw near,   praise him with
all   that   is   need - ful hath been   grant - ed   in
all   the   al - might - y   can   do,   he   who   with
sound from   his   peo - ple   a - gain-   glad - ly   for,

C#m   Bsus⁴   B   E

glad   a - dor - a   -   tion!
what   he   or - dain   -   eth?
love   doth   be - friend   thee.
aye,   we   a - dore   him.

A psalm for giving thanks

Psalm 100

Shout for joy to the Lord, all the earth.
Worship the Lord with gladness;
come before him with joyful songs.
Know that the Lord is God.
It is he who made us, and we are his;
we are his people, the sheep of his pasture.

Enter his gates with thanksgiving
and his courts with praise;
give thanks to him and praise his name.
For the Lord is good
and his love endures for ever;
his faithfulness continues
through all generations.

118   Prepare The Way

Isaiah 40 & 41
A. Piercy & C. Groves
Arr. Alison Berry

Steady ♩ = 120

1. Pre-pare the way   for the Lord;   make straight his
2. Do you not know?   Have you not heard?   He sits en-

path   in the wil-der-ness-   a high-way for our
throned   a - bove the earth   and stretch-es out the

God:_____   ev-ery val-ley   shall be raised
hea - vens: lift up your voice_   and with a

up,   and ev-ery moun-tain__   be made low;   and the
shout,   come, lift it up:_____   don't be a - fraid-   and the

119 Purify My Heart
(Refiner's Fire)

Brian Doerkson

Prayerfully ♩ = 80

Capo 2(D)

1. Pur - i - fy __ my heart, __ let me be as gold and __ pre - cious sil - ver; pur - i - fy __ my heart, __ let me be as gold, pure __ gold. Re - fin - er's fire, __

2. Pur - i - fy __ my heart, __ cleanse me from with- in and __ make me ho - ly; pur - i - fy __ my heart, __ cleanse me from my sin, deep with - in. Re - fin - er's fire, __

Capo 2 D.

120   Sing To The Lord
(Awaken The Dawn)

With a lilt ♩. = 60

Stuart Garrard

1. Sing to the Lord__ with all of your heart, sing of the glo - ry that's
2. Sing to the Lord__ with all of your mind, with un - der - stand -ing give

due to his name; sing to the Lord___ with all of your soul,
thanks to the King; sing to the Lord___ with all of your strength,

join all of hea -ven and earth to pro -claim: You are the Lord,__ the
liv -ing our lives as a praise of - fer -ing.

sa -viour of all,__ God of cre - a - tion, we praise you.

We sing the songs that a-wa-ken the dawn, God of cre-a-tion, we praise you.

Psalm 33

Sing joyfully to the Lord, you righteous;
it is fitting for the upright to praise him.
Praise the Lord with the harp;
make music to him on the ten-stringed lyre.
Sing to him a new song;
play skilfully, and shout for joy.

121 Such Love

1. Such love, pure as the whit-est snow,
   such love, weeps for the shame I know,
   such love, pay-ing the debt I owe—
   O Je-sus, such love!

2. Such love, still-ing my rest-less-ness,
   such love, fill-ing my emp-ti-ness,
   such love, show-ing me ho-li-ness—
   O Je-sus, such love!

3. Such love, springs from e-ter-ni-ty,
   such love, stream-ing through his-to-ry,
   such love, foun-tain of life to me—
   O Je-sus, such love!

122 Thank You For Saving Me

With a steady rhythm ♩ = 100

Martin Smith

1. Thank you for sa-ving me— what__ can I__ say?
2. Mer-cy and grace are mine, for-giv-en is my__ sin-

You are my ev-ery-thing, I will sing your praise.
Je-sus my on-ly hope, the sav-iour of the world.

You shed your blood for me— what__ can I__ say?
'Great is the Lord,' we cry, 'God, let your king-dom__ come!'

You took my sin and shame, a sin-ner called by name.__
Your word has let me see, thank you for sav-ing me.__

Great is the Lord,

great is the Lord! For we know your

truth has set us free— you've

set your hope in me.

Thank you for sav - ing me— what can I say?

123 The Cross Has Said It All

Psalm 103: 11-12. Ephesians 3:18
Matt Redman & Martin Smith

The
cross has said it all, the cross has said it all..
cross has said it all, the cross has said it all..

I can't de - ny what you
I ne - ver re - cog - nised

have shown, the cross speaks of a God
your touch un - til I met you at

of love; there dis - played for all
the cross; we are fal - len, dust

to __ see, _____ Je - sus Christ, _____ our ___ on -
to __ dust, ____ how could you _____ do ___ this_

- ly __ hope, _____ a mess - age of _____ the ____ Fa -
for __ us? ____ Son of God ____ shed ___ pre -

- ther's ___ heart: _____ 'Come, my child - ren, ____ come_
- cious ___ blood, _____ who can com - pre - hend_

__ on ___ home.' _____ As
__ this ___ love? _____

high as the heavens ____ are a - bove ___ the ___ earth, ___ so

high is the mea - sure of ___ your ___ great ___ love; ___ as

far as the east ___ is ___ from ___ the ___ west, ___ so

far have you ta - ken our ___ sins ___ from ___ us. ___ As

from ___ us. ___ 2. The

from ___ us. ___ How high, how wide, how deep,

124 The Crucible For Silver

Martin J. Smith
Arr. D. J. Langford

1. The cru - ci - ble __ for sil - ver, and the fur - nace __ for gold, __ but the
2. Fa - ther, take __ our off'e - ring, with our song we hum - bly praise you; you have

Lord tests the heart __ of this child. Stand - ing in __ all pu - ri - ty, God, our
brought your ho - ly fire to our lips. Stand - ing in __ your beau - ty, Lord, your __

pas - sion is __ for ho - li - ness: lead us to __ the se - cret place __ of __
gift to us __ is ho - li - ness: lead us to __ the place __ where we __ can __

125 The Day Of The Streams

Dave Bilbrough &
Andy Piercy

Lively ♩ = 120

The day of the streams is ov - er, __ the time of the ri - ver is here; the day of the streams is ov - er, __ the time of the ri - ver is here. *Fine*

1. I hear the
2. There is a

1. sound of a migh - ty ri - ver, of rush - ing
2. time I __ know is com - ing when all God's

wa - ter run - ning free ___
peo - ple join as one; ___

to ev - ery land, through ev - ery bor - der, ___ flow - ing
it will be - come a great a - wak - en - ing, bring - ing

out a - cross this earth.
life to all the world.

3.

And the ri - ver is flow-ing- get - ting wi - der and wi - der,

deep - er and deep - er as it flows from the throne; ___ and the

leaves on the trees ___ are for the heal - ing of the na - tions, it's as

D.C. al Fine

clear as crys - tal, it's the wa - ter of life.

126 The God Of Abraham Praise

Words: Transcribed by M. Lyon,
adapted by T. Olivers
Music: from a synagogue melody
for the Yigdal (doxology)

1. The God of Abra - ham praise who reigns en - throned a - bove; the an - cient of e - ter - nal days and God of love! The Lord, the great I
2. To him we lift our voice at whose su - preme com - mand from death we rise to gain the joys at his right hand: we all on earth for -
3. Though na - ture's strength de - cay, and earth and hell with - stand, at his com - mand we fight our way to Can - aan's land: the wat - er's deep we
4. He by his name has sworn - on this we shall de - pend, and as on eag - les' wings up - bourne to heaven as - cend: there we shall see his
5. There rules the Lord our king, the Lord our right - eous - ness, vic - tor - ious o - ver death and sin, the prince of peace: on Zi - on's sac - red
6. Tri - umph - ant hosts on high give thanks e - ter - nal - ly and 'Ho - ly, ho - ly, ho - ly' cry, 'great Tri - ni - ty!' Hail Abra - ham's God and

D　B⁷　Em　C　Em/G　Am　Bsus⁴　B

AM,　by　earth ___ and ___ heaven con - fessed- ___　we
- sake-　its ___　wis - dom, ___ fame,　and　pow - er;　the
pass　with ___　Je - sus　in　our　view, ___　and
face,　his ___　po - wer we ___ shall　a - dore, ___　and
height　his ___　king - dom ___　he　main - tains, ___　and
ours!　one ___　migh - ty ___　hymn　we　raise, ___　all

Em/G B　Em　Am/C Em/G　Am/C G/B　Am Em/G Am　Em/B Bsus⁴　Em

bow　be - fore his　ho - ly ___　name　for ___　ev - er　blessed.
God　of　Is - rael　we　shall ___　make　our ___　shield and　tower.
through the howl - ing wild - er - ness　our ___　path pur - sue.
sing　the won - ders　of　his ___　grace　for ___　ev - er - more.
glor - ious with his　saints　in ___　light　for ___　ev - er　reigns.
power and ma - jes - ty　be ___　yours and ___　end - less　praise!

Praise response

from Psalm 113

Praise the Lord, you servants of the Lord;
praise the name of the Lord.

Blest be the name of the Lord;
both now and evermore. Amen.

127 The Heavens Shall Declare

The hea-vens shall de-clare the glo-ry of__ his name; all cre-a-tion bows_____ at the com-ing of__ the King. Ev-ery eye__ shall see, ev-ery heart__ will

128 The World Is Looking For A Hero
(Champion)

Noel & Tricia Richards
Arr. L. Hills

1. The world is look-ing for a he-ro, ____
2. The Lord al-might-ty is our he-ro, ____

we know the great-est one of all:
he breaks the strang-le-hold of sin;

the migh-ty ru-ler of the na-tions ____
through Je-sus' love we fear no ev-il, ____

King of kings and Lord of lords,
powers of dark-ness flee from him;

129 There Is A Redeemer

Melody Green
Arr. David Peacock

1. There is a Re - deem - er,
2. Je - sus, my Re - deem - er,
3. When I stand in glo - ry

Jes - us, God's own son, _____ pre - cious Lamb of
name a - bove all names, _____ pre - cious Son of
I will see his face, _____ and there I'll serve my

God, Mes - si - ah, ho - ly One.
God, Mes - si - ah, Lamb for sin - ners slain:
king for ev - er in that ho - ly place.

Thank you, O my Fa - ther, for giv - ing us your

Son,_____ and leav - ing your Spi - rit till the

work_ on_ earth is done. done.

Greeting each other
from Galatians 6

Peace and mercy
to the people of God:

**the grace of our Lord Jesus Christ
be with your spirit.**

130   There Is Power In The Name Of Jesus

With a driving rhythm ♩ = 150

Noel Richards

1. There is power in the name of Je - sus-
(2) power in the name of Je - sus,

we be - lieve in his name.
like a sword in our hands.

We have called on the name of Je - sus:
We de - clare in the name of Je - sus:

we are saved, we are saved! At his
we shall stand, we shall stand! At his

name the de - mons flee, at his
name, God's en - em - ies shall be

name cap - tives are freed; _____ for there
crushed be - neath our feet; _____ for there

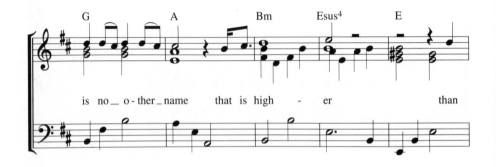

is no _ o - ther _ name that is high - er than

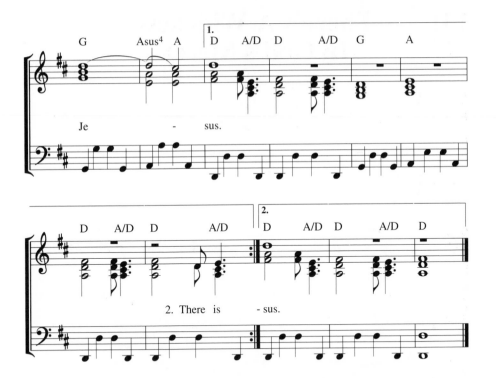

131 There's A Wideness In God's Mercy

After F.W. Faber
Geoff Baker

♩ = 120

There's a wide - ness in ___ God's mer - cy that is

wi - der than ___ the great - est sea; and so I know ___ it

co - vers e - ven me. ___ There's a

depth to his ___ com - pas - sion that is deep - er than ___ I'll

un - der - stand; and so my life ___ is safe with - in ___ his

132 There's A Wind A-Blowing

David Ruis

1. There's _____ a wind a - blow - ing _____ all _____ a - cross the land, _____ a fra - grant breeze of hea - ven _____ blow - ing once a - gain. _____
2. There's _____ a rain a - pour - ing _____ sho - wers from a - bove, _____ mer - cy drops are com - ing, _____ mer - cy drops of love: _____
3. There's _____ a fire ___ burn - ing _____ fall - ing from the sky- _____ awe - some tongues of fire _____ con - - su - ming you and me. _____

come and blow o - ver me.
come and pour o - ver me.
come and burn o - ver me.

me.

133 There's No-One Like You

Eddie Espinosa

Lyrics:

There's no-one _ like you, my _ Lord, _____ no - one _ could
you, my _ Lord, _____ no - one _ could

take your place; ___ my heart beats _ to wor - ship _ you,
take · your place. ___ I long for _ your pre - sence _ Lord -

I live just _ to seek your _ face. _____ There's no - one _ like
to serve you _ is my re - ward. _____ There's no - one _ like

134   Thine Be The Glory

Words: E.L. Budry
Tr. R.B. Hoyle
Music: G.F. Handel
Arr. C. Norton

1. Thine be the glo - ry, ri - sen, con - quering Son,
2. Lo, Je - sus meets us, ri - sen from the tomb!
3. No more we doubt thee glor - ious prince of life;

end - less is the vic - tory thou o'er death hast won.
Lov - ing - ly he greets us, scat - ters fear and gloom.
life is nought with - out thee: aid us in our strife;

135 Throughout The Earth Your Glory

(Lord Come And Reign)

James Wright

1. Through-out the earth your glo-ry will come- a day of power, of sal-va-tion;___ to thirs-ty hearts your ri-vers will run, __ chang-ing lives for the glo-ry of God.___ From Sa-tan's hold this

2. Up-on the earth may your king-dom come,__ with-in our lives may your will be done;__ un-der the reign of Je-sus, the Son,_ we will live for the glo-ry of God.___ The gates of heaven are

land will be free, ___ the deaf will hear, the blind ___ will see ___
o - pen wide ___ to bless this land, to turn back the tide, ___

to walk in truth, in vic - tor -y- ___ to ___ live for the glo - ry of God.
to wel - come in his glo - ri - ous bride, ___ to ___ live for the glo- ry of God. _

___ Lord, come and reign ___ by the power of your Spi - rit, show-er this land _

___ with your ri - vers of life _____ that Je - sus, the Son _

would be glo - ri - fied___ with -
in the heart of your bride-___ Lord, come and reign.

1.
Lord, come and reign.

2.
Lord, come and reign.

Psalm 89

I will sing of
the Lord's great love
for ever;
with my mouth
I will make your faithfulness known
through all generations.
I will declare that
your love stands firm
for ever,
that you established
your faithfulness
in heaven itself.

136 To Be In Your Presence

(My Desire)

Noel Richards
Arr. L. Evans

1. To be in your pres-ence, to sit at your feet, where your love sur-rounds me, and makes me com-plete:__ This is my__ de-sire, O__ Lord, this is my__ de-sire;

2. To rest in your pres-ence, not rush-ing a-way, to cher-ish each mom-ent-here I would stay:__

this is my ___ de - sire,   O ___ Lord,   this is my ___ de-

To end

- sire.

137   Wake Up O Sleeper

Ephesians 5:8-17
Graham Kendrick

Wake up, O sleep - er, and rise from the dead, ___

1. and Christ will shine on you. ___

2. and Christ will shine on you. ___

1. Once you were dark -ness but now ___ you are light, ___
2. This is the beau - ti - ful fruit ___ of the light, ___
3. As days get dark - er, take care ___ how you live: ___

now you are light in the Lord._____
the good, the right - eous, the true:_____
not as un - wise but as wise;_____

So, as true child - ren of light,_____ you must live_____
let us dis - cov - er what pleas - es the Lord_____
mak - ing the most of each mo - ment he gives_____

show-ing the glo - ry of God._____
in ev-ery-thing that we do._____
and press-ing on for the prize._____

138

We Are Marching
In The Light Of God

Words: African origin
collected and edited by Anders Nyberg
Music: African melody scored by
Norman K. B. Ljungsbro and Lars Parkman

G   C   D   G

Oh ____ we are

march-ing,   march-ing,) we are   march-ing in the light of God!
liv-ing,   liv-ing,) we are   liv-ing in the love of God!
mov-ing   mov-ing,) we are   mov-ing in the power of God!

Affirming our faith
from Galatians 3

We are children of God:
we are justified by faith.

We are baptised into Christ:
we are clothed with him.

We are neither Jew nor Greek,
slave nor free,
male nor female:
we are all one in Christ Jesus.
Amen.

139 We Believe

Graham Kendrick
Arr. Chris Norton

1. We believe in God the Father, maker of the universe, and in Christ his Son, our saviour, come to us by virgin birth. We believe he died to save us, bore our sins, was cru - ci -fied; then from death he rose vic-tor-ious, a-

2. We believe he sends his Spirit on his church with gifts of power; God, his word of truth af - firm - ing, sends us to the nations now. He will come a - gain in glo - ry, judge the liv - ing and the dead: ev - ery knee shall bow be -fore him, __

140 We Have A Great Priest

Meditatively ♩ = 60

D. Clifton

1. We have a great priest o-ver the house of God, so let us draw near to God with a sin - cere heart in full as - sur - ance, as - sur-ance of our faith, hav - ing our

hearts___ touched to cleanse us from all guilt, _____ for he who__ prom-ised ____ is faith-ful, for he who__ pro-mised___ is faith - ful, is faith - ful to me. 2. Give me a pure__ heart:_____ hold-ing to your__ hope, _____ the hope I pro-

141 We Have Called On You

Stuart Garrard

1. We have called on you, Lord, and you have heard us;
2. You have stretched out your hand, and you have touched us;

we have called on your name, and
sent us your ho - ly fire, and

you have an - swered.
you have purged us.

Mer - cy has
Light___ has

tri - umphed o - ver judg - ment, ___
tri - umphed o - ver dark - ness, ___

a liv - ing sac - ri - fice-__ emp - ty and
read - y to __ be filled __ with your pow - er.

The Grace

The grace of our Lord Jesus Christ,
and the love of God,
and the fellowship of the Holy Spirit
be with us all evermore.
Amen.

142 We Want To See Jesus Lifted High

Lively ♩ = 160

Doug Horley

We want to see Je - sus lif - ted high- a ban-ner that flies a-cross this land; that all men might see the truth and know he is the way to hea - ven. We want to see, (We're gon - na) we want to see, (we're gon - na) we want to see Je - sus lift - ed high. (we're gon - na)

143 We Worship And Adore You

Andy Piercy
Words for v3: Cecil F. Alexander
Arr. Alison Berry

We wor - ship and __ a - dore __ you, __ Lord-
hear us when __ we __ call, __ for there __ is __ no god __ a - bove __
__ you, __ you are the Lord __ of __ all. __ 1. But

how can we __ be - gin __ to __ ex - press what's on __ our __ hearts?
__ of men __ and an - gels __ we need, to sing __ your __ praise, __

There are no words en-ough, Lord, for
so that we may glo - ri - fy your name through

us to e - ven start. 2. The tongues 3. There was no oth - er good
heaven's e - ter - nal days.

e - nough to pay the price of sin, you

on - ly, could un - lock the gate of heaven and let us in.

So, we wor - ship and a - dore

144 We've Had A Light Shine In Our Midst

Matt Redman

We've had a light shine in our midst, we've felt your pre-sence, we've known your peace; and though this bless-ing comes to us free, it car-ries a chal-lenge to go. We've had a feast laid on for us; you have com-mand-ed: bring in the lost. There's food for all, an-y who'd come-

what - ever the ___ cost; _____ time is so short,

we can - not ___ squan - der this ___ love. _____

Sure - ly the time

has come

to bring the har -

145 Well I Hear They're Singing In The Street

(I've Found Jesus)

Martin Smith
Arr. L. Hills

Well, I hear they're sing-ing in the streets that Je-sus is a - live, and
(2) feel like danc-ing in the streets 'cause Je-sus is a - live, to

all cre - a - tion shouts a - loud that Je-sus is a - live; now
join with all who ce - le - brate that Je-sus is a - live. The

sure - ly we can all be changed 'cause Je - sus is a - live; and
joy of God is in this town 'cause Je-sus is a - live; for

ev-ery-bo-dy here can know that Je - sus is __ a - live. __ And
ev-ery-bo-dy's seen the truth that Je - sus is __ a - live. __

I will live for all __ my days to raise a ban - ner of truth and light, __

__ to sing a-bout __ my sav-iour's love and the

best thing that hap-pened- it was the day I met you. I've found

Je - sus, I've found Je - sus,

146 Well, I Was In Need

Russell Fragar

Well, I was in ___ need, I need-ed a friend I was a - lone, I need-ed a hand; ___ I was go-ing down, but some-one res - cued me. ___

mer-cies are new ev - ery day; ___ I get down to pray ___ and then ___

help is on its way.

My God cares ___ too much ___ to ___ say, ___ his mer-cies are ___ new ev-

- ery day; I get down to pray _____ and then ___

help is on its way.

147 When I Look Into Your Holiness

Wayne & Cathy Perrin
Arr. G Baker

♩ = 80

When I look in-to your ho-li-ness, — when I gaze in-to your love-li- ness, when all things that sur-round be-come sha-dows — in the light of you; — when I've found the joy — of reach-ing your heart, — when my will be-comes — en-thralled with your love, when all

things that sur -round be-come sha -dows _ in the light of you:_____

I wor- ship you, _____ I wor -ship you, _____

the rea - son I live ____ is to wor - ship you; _____

I wor - ship you, _____ I wor - ship you, _____

the rea -son I live ____ is to wor - ship you. _____

148 When I Survey

Words: Issac Watts
Music adapted by E. Miller

1. When I___ sur - vey the wond - rous cross on
2. For - bid___ it, Lord, that I should boast save
3. See from___ his head, his hands, his feet, sor -
4. Were the___ whole realm of na - ture mine, that

which the prince of glo - ry died, ___ my
in the cross of Christ___ my God: ___ the
- row and love flow ming - led down: ___ when
were an of - fering far___ too small; ___ love

rich - est gain I count___ as loss and
ve - ry things that charm___ me most- I
did such love and sor - row meet or
so a - maz - ing, so___ di - vine, de-

pour con - tempt on all___ my pride.
sac - ri - fice them to___ his blood.
thorns com - pose so rich___ a crown?
- mands my soul, my life, ___ my all!

149 Who Will Call Him King Of Kings

Greg Nelson, Bob Farrell,
& Sandi Patti Helvering
Adapted and arranged
by Martin Alfsen

1. Who will call him king of kings, — who will call him Lord of Lords, —
2. We will call him king of kings, — we will call him Lord of Lords, —

— who will call him Prince of Peace, — such a won-der-ful coun-
— we will call him Prince of Peace, — such a won-der-ful coun-

-sel-lor, migh-ty God? -ty God.
-sel-lor, migh-ty God.

3. I will call him king of kings, — I will call him Lord of Lords.

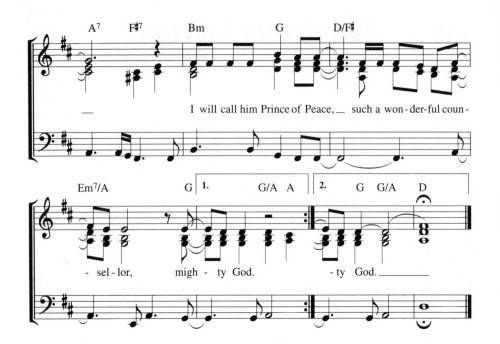

I will call him Prince of Peace, ___ such a won-der-ful coun-

- sel-lor,   migh - ty God.

1.

2.   - ty God. _____

150 Yes, God Is Good In Earth And Sky

John Hampden Gurney
Music from Templi Carmina

♩ = 120

1. Yes, God is good: in earth and sky, from o - cean
2. The sun that keeps his track - less way and down - ward
3. The joy - ful birds pro - long the strain, their song with
4. I hear it in the rush - ing breeze, the hills that
5. 'Yes, God is good,' all na - ture says by God's own
6. For all your gifts we bless you, Lord, but chief - ly

depths and spread - ing wood, ten thou - sand voi - ces seem to
pours his gold - en flood, night's spark - ling hosts, all seem to
ev - ery spring re - newed; the air we breathe, and fall - ing
have for ag - es stood, the echo - ing sky and roar - ing
hand with speech en - dued; and we in loud - er notes of
for our heav - enly food; your pardon - ing grace, your quick - ening

cry: 'God made us all, and God is good!'
say in ac - cents clear that God is good.
rain, each soft - ly whis - pers: 'God is good.'
seas, all swell the cho - rus: 'God is good.'
praise shall sing for joy that God is good.
word, these prompt our song that God is good!

151 You Are Mighty

Craig Musseau

Soulfully ♩ = 93

You are migh - ty, you are ho - ly, ___ you are awe - some ___ in your pow - er; ___ you have ris - sen, you have con - quered, ___ you have bea - ten ___ the power ___ of ___ death. ___

152 You Are My Passion

Noel & Tricia Richards
Arr. Caroline Bonnett

You are my pas - sion, love of my life-
friend and com - pan - ion - my lov - er.
All of my be - ing longs for your touch,
with all my heart I love you.

Now will you draw ___ me close to you,

gath - er me in your arms?

Let me hear the beat - ing of your heart,

O my Je - sus, O my Je - sus.

153   You Gave Up Your Life

Charlie Groves
Arr. Alison Berry

154 You Have Rescued Me

Jonny Baker

♩ = 120

Lyrics under the staves:

You have res-cued me, giv-en me joy and set me free; re-stored my hu-man-i-ty you have res-cued me.

1. I lacked pur - pose, di - rec - tion and mean - ing
2. My heart was self - ish, proud and de - ceit - ful;
(3) im - age in me was twist - ed and brok - en, but

could-n't make sense___ of liv-ing in this___ world;_____
though I had tried,___ I could-n't seem to___ change;_____
you have be - gun___ to make me___ new;_____

each way I turned___ there seemed no so - lu - tion- then you
trapped in my sin___ and dis - il - lu - sioned, then you
in your___ plan___ to free the cre - a - tion- thanks that

came and res - cued me.___
came and res - cued me.___ You have
you in - clud - ed me.___

res-cued me,___ giv-en me joy___ and set me free; _ re-

- stored my hu-man-i - ty-___ you have res-cued me.___ 3.Your

155 You Laid Aside Your Majesty

I real-ly want to wor-ship you, my Lord; you have won my
heart and I am yours for ev-er and ev-er: I will
love you. You are the on-ly one who died for me, gave your life
to set me free, so I lift my voice to you in a-do-
-ra tion.

Twice then repeat chorus.

156 You Resist The Proud, Embrace The Humble
(Lifted Up)

Kevin Prosch

For inward peace

O Lord, your way is perfect:
help us, we pray,
always to trust in your goodness;
that walking with you in faith,
and following you in all simplicity,
we may possess quiet and contented minds,
and leave all our worries with you,
because you care for us;
for the sake of Jesus Christ our Lord.

Amen.

157 Your Hand O God Has Guided

Words: Edward Plumptre
Music: Basil Harwood
Arr. Christopher Norton

Steadily ♩ = 120

1. Your hand, O God, has guid - ed your flock, from age___ to age; your faithful - ness is writ - ten on his-tory's ev - ery page;

(2) her - alds brought the gos - pel to great - est as___ to least; they sum - moned us to has - ten and share the great_king's feast;

(3) ma - ny days of dark - ness, through ma - ny scenes_ of strife, the faith - ful few fought brave - ly to guard the na - tion's life;

(4) we, shall we be faith - less? Shall hearts fail, hands_ hang down? Shall we e - vade the con - flict and throw a - way_ the crown?

(5) mer - cy will not fail us nor leave your work_ un - done; with your right hand to help us, the vic - tory shall_ be won;

page. They knew your per - fect good - ness, whose
feast. And this was all their teach - ing in
life. Their gos - pel of re - demp - tion- sin
crown? Not so! In God's deep coun - sels some
won. And then by earth and hea - ven your

deeds we now re - cord; and both to this bear wit - ness: one
ev - ery deed and word; to all a - like pro - claim - ing: one
par - doned, hope re - stored; was all in this en - fold - ed: one
bet - ter thing is stored; we will main - tain, un - flinch - ing, one
name shall be a - dored; and this shall be their an - them: one

church, one faith, one Lord. 2. Your
church, one faith, one Lord. 3. Through
church, one faith, one Lord. 4. And
church, one faith, one Lord. 5. Your
church, one faith, one Lord

158 Your Love Looks After Me
(For The Rest Of My Days)

Contemplative Ballad ♩ = 96

Chris Falson

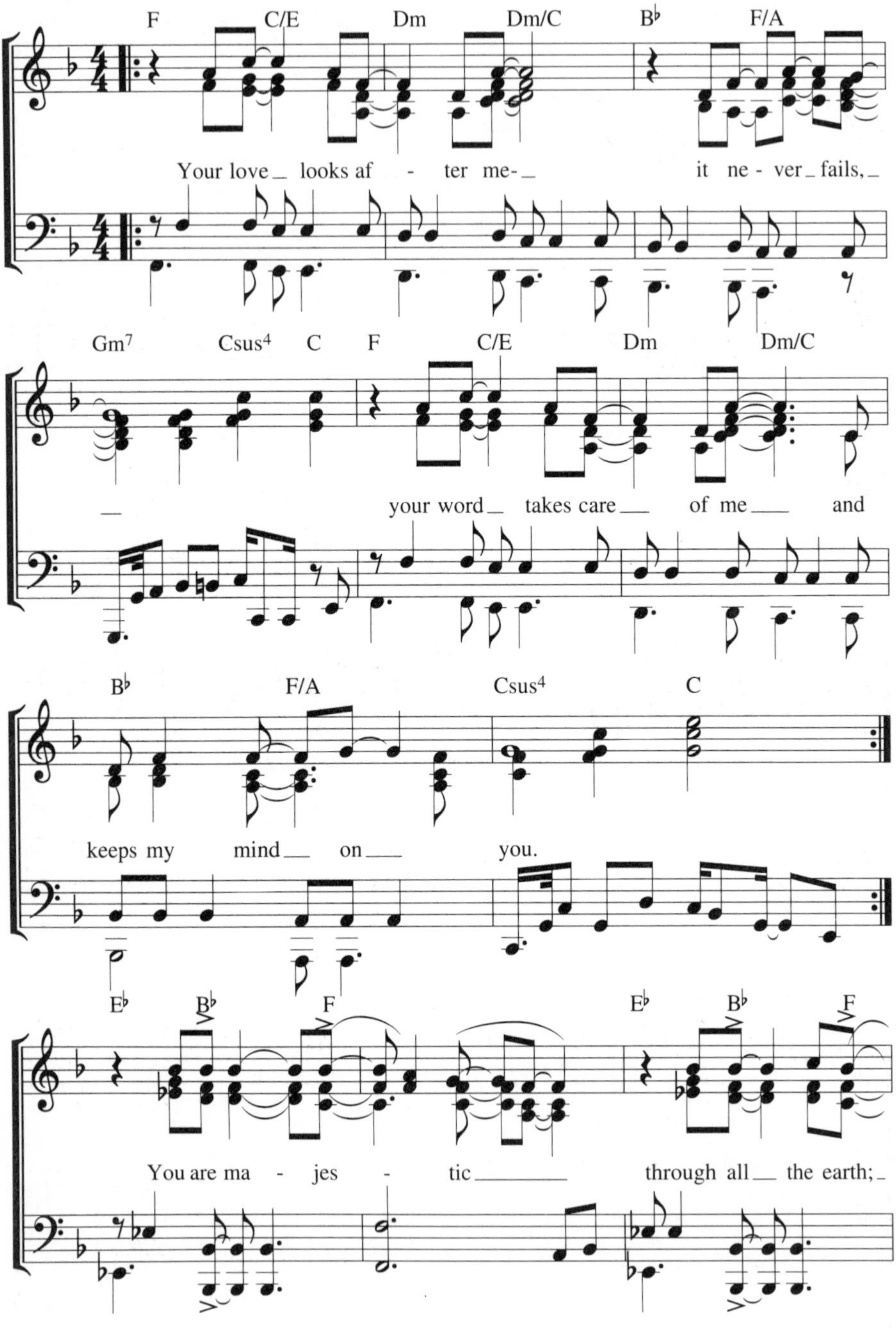

F C/E Dm Dm/C B♭ F/A
Your love _ looks af - ter me- _ it ne - ver _ fails, _
Gm7 Csus4 C F C/E Dm Dm/C
_ your word _ takes care _ of me _ and
B♭ F/A Csus4 C
keeps my mind _ on _ you.
E♭ B♭ F E♭ B♭ F
You are ma - jes - tic _ through all _ the earth; _

for the rest of my days, _____ for the

rest of my days. _____

Praise response

from Psalm 92

It is good to praise you, Lord:
and make music to your name.

To proclaim your constant love in the morning:
and tell your faithfulness in the evening.

For you, O Lord, are exalted for ever.
Amen.

159 Your Love O Lord

Psalm 34
Peggy Caswell

1. Your love, O Lord, it reach-es to the hea-
2. Your name, O Lord, it is a migh-ty tow-

- vens; your faith-ful-ness, it
- wer; your glo-ry, it

reach-es to the skies; your
cov-ers all the earth;

praise___ your ho - ly___ name___ that my heart may

sing to you-___ I will ex - alt you, O___ Lord.___

INDEX

Song titles differing from first lines are in italics

Index of prayers and liturgy

Spring Harvest is an annual event bringing together thousands of Christians from many different backgrounds.

At the heart of the event is worship - praise to God expressed in a variety of styles. There is also high quality Bible teaching, practical seminars, fellowship and leisure activities.

Interested? For a free brochure, send this card or call Spring Harvest Customer Service on:

01825 769000

Spring Harvest. A registered charity

PLEASE SEND ME

☐ A free Spring Harvest colour brochure

☐ Details about help and discounts for group organisers

☐ Details of music products (Live Worship, New Songs, Kids Praise)

Name (Mr/Mrs/Ms) ....

Address ....

Postcode .... Telephone ....

M96

2

Spring Harvest
Freepost (TN 6008)
14 Horsted Square
Uckfield
East Sussex
TN22 1BR